Learning About Measurement

Grades 1-3

Written by Melanie Komar
Illustrated by Keith Milne & S&S Learning Materials

ISBN 1-55035-703-4
Copyright 2003
Revised March 2006
All Rights Reserved * Printed in Canada

Published in the United States by:
On the Mark Press
3909 Witmer Road PMB 175
Niagara Falls, New York
14305
www.onthemarkpress.com

Other Math Units

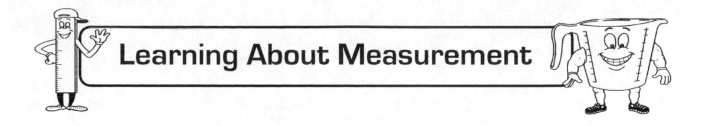

Table of Contents

Introduction

Children live in a world where things are measured. At the moment of birth, they are measured and weighed. Their height is measured in notches on the wall as they grow. Children will ask, "How far away is the park?" They notice if their brother has a bigger piece of cake.

Children often make spontaneous discoveries while manipulating objects; therefore, a wide range of materials should be provided. The teacher should encourage exploration.

This unit was designed for the teacher and the students so that the many concepts pertaining to measurement can be taught, practiced and reinforced. It contains many written and manipulative activities.

Objectives

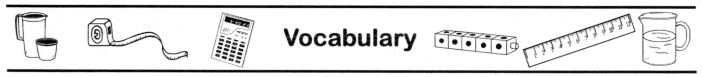

1. Students will understand measurable attributes, the concept of a unit (of measure) and the process of measuring.

2. Students will make and use measurement in problems and every day situations.

3. Students will make and use estimates in measurement situations.

Vocabulary

Linear Words:

length, height, tall, taller, tallest, short, shorter, shortest, long, longer, longest, far, farther, farthest

Area Words:

cover, area, squares, bits, units, grid, acres, rods

Mass or Weight Words:

weight, mass, ounce, pound, heavy, heavier, heaviest, light, lighter, lightest, ton

Volume and Capacity Words:

fill, pour, empty, full, container, level, holds, quart, pint, stack, cube, cubic inch, space ounce, gallon, teaspoon, tablespoon, cup

Other Measurement Words:

estimate, measure, count, foot, inch, feet, yard, mile

Teacher Input Suggestions

1. Teachers should completely read over this unit before implementing any activities into their classroom. Many activities require prior set-up by the teacher (including the supply of certain materials).

2. Students need many opportunities to experience hands-on exploration of materials. Many students have difficulty understanding the concepts of area and volume. Textbooks have pictures that don't always allow young students to grasp the ideas. Many of the activities suggested in this unit encourage the hands-on approach to stimulate and engage the students.

3. Begin collecting any of the various items listed below. Place an empty box in a specified place in the classroom. Encourage your students to bring items from home as well. These items can be used for estimation activities, comparisons and manipulative activities.

   String, rulers, yard sticks, yarn, sports equipment (bats, golf clubs, etc.) strips of paper (such as adding machine tape), chart paper, various lengths of wooden sticks, connecting cubes, paper clips, graph paper, squared graph paper, geo-paper, various scales (beamer balances, triple beam balances, bathroom scale), building blocks, items to pour (sand, water, rice, dried peas, pasta, etc.) eye droppers, funnels, tubes, containers of all sizes (jars, bottles, bowls, pails, cans, spoons, cartons, etc.), boxes of all sizes, graduated beakers, small cups (e.g. medicine or dixie cups)

4. Set up a center for the strand of measurement that is being taught. It is recommended that the strands are taught in the following order: linear measurement, area, mass or weight, volume and capacity. Put out materials that will allow the students to explore measurement.

5. Set up a store to encourage role playing and discussion of mass or weight, capacity, size, etc.

6. If your classroom doesn't already have a sand and water table, consider setting these up at the Math Center.

7. Brainstorm with your students important vocabulary words for each of the different strands of measurement (i.e. linear, mass or weight, area, volume and capacity). The students can make a pictionary for each strand, using the important vocabulary words.

8. Ask the students to find the length, mass or weight, area, capacity of various items.

9. While learning about **area**, have the students make a collage of pictures from magazines that show things "covering" other things, i.e. rugs, curtains, bedspreads, grass, etc.

10. While learning about **mass or weight**, fill containers of equal size and shape with a variety of different materials (flour, pasta, rice, toothpicks, sand, water, cotton, popsicle sticks, lego, etc.). The students can estimate, and then weigh, each container to determine which material was the lightest and heaviest. It is recommended that approximately five containers filled with different items are available for comparison.

11. Estimate the mass or weight of several student volunteers (please note that some students, particularly those amongst the heaviest or lightest in the class may be sensitive about their size; therefore, it is recommended that only those students who volunteer be weighed in front of the class). Find their actual mass or weight.

12. Encourage students to bring packages from home that have the mass or weight of the package in ounces or pounds. Discuss why some things are weighed in ounces and others are weighed in pounds.

13. When learning about **volume and capacity**, encourage the students to bring containers (cans, boxes, bottles, baskets, bags, etc.) from home. Discuss various ways to sort the containers (i.e. large/small; paper/plastic/metal; lid/no lid; see through, etc.). When you are finished using the containers, the students can use them to make sculptures.

14. Do some baking and discuss how important measurement is in the various steps. Use the vocabulary words (volume, fill, pour, cup, tablespoon, container, full, "how much", etc.).

15. Estimation is an important skill to develop. Encourage reasonable estimation regularly (while discouraging "wild guesses"). Have an "estimation jar" in your classroom. Each Monday, fill the jar with different objects. At some point throughout the week, the students can put their guess on a piece of paper with their name, and put them in the box. On Friday, count the objects and give a sticker to the closest guesser. Keep a chart of previous objects and the number of them that filled the jar. It's a good idea to glue one of the objects to the chart to remind the students of the size of the object. They should be able to figure out that if the jar held nine marshmallows last week, and the blocks in it this week are similar size, then "nine" would be a reasonable guess.

16. Brainstorm items used for measurement at home and at school. Standard units may be discussed at this time. Discuss why we use standard units. Make a list of their ideas, and add to the list as your learning about measurement progresses. As a class, indicate beside each measurement whether it is used as a measure of length, volume, or mass (weight). You may wish to include clocks, calendars, thermometers, and even money as units of measurement, although they are not included in this unit.

17. Make a bulletin board of pictures of items used for measuring. Actual items can also be attached to the board.

18. Find the mass (weight) of some popcorn kernels. Pop the popcorn. Ask the students if they think that the mass (weight) will be less, the same, or more. Find the mass (weight) again; make sure the same container is used to hold the popcorn both times. Were they correct? Discuss.

19. To evaluate the accomplishments of the students, the teacher should observe them as they work, make anecdotal records, interview individual students, have discussions with them and review their written work. Students should also self-evaluate their own learning and progress.

20. Prior to directing the students to Linear Activity 8, which involves measuring the **circumference** of different sized sports balls, it is suggested that you perform the following activity as a whole class: Take a variety of different sized pumpkins (or beach balls, watermelons, etc.). Ask the students to guess which pumpkin (or other item) will have the smallest **diameter** and put them in order up to the largest. Then, show them how to measure around the *middle* with a measuring tape. Compare estimated answers with actual results. If you do use pumpkins for this activity, measure and graph the vertical lines on each pumpkin. Discuss the results.

Stories About Measurement

Aber, L.W. (2001). <u>Carrie Measures Up</u>. New York: Kane Press. ISBN 1575651009

Adler, D. (1999). <u>How Tall, How Short, How Faraway</u>. New York: Holiday House. ISBN 1823413756

Cato, S. (1998). <u>Measuring</u>. Minneapolis, MN: Carolrhoda Books. ISBN 1575053233

DeRubertis, B. (2000). <u>Lulu's Lemonade</u>. New York: Kane Press. ISBN 1575650932

Hightower, S. (1997). <u>Twelve Snails To One Lizard: a tale of mischief and measurement</u>. New York: Simon and Schuster. ISBN 0689804520

Leedy, L. (1997). <u>Measuring Penny</u>. New York: Henry Holt. ISBN 080503603

Ling, B. (1997). <u>The Fattest, Tallest, Biggest Snowman Ever</u>. New York: Scholastic. ISBN 0590972847

Murphy, S. (1999). <u>Room for Ripley</u>. New York: Harper Collins. ISBN 0064467244

Murphy, S. (1999). <u>Super Sandcastle Sunday</u>. New York: Harper Collins. ISBN 0060276134

Patilla, P. (2000). <u>Measuring</u>. Des Plaines, IL: Heinemann Library. ISBN 1575726952

Pluckrose, H.A. (1988). <u>Know About Length</u>. New York: Franklin Watts. ISBN 0516454536.

Pluckrose, H.A. (1988). <u>Weight</u>. New York: Franklin Watts. ISBN 051654609

Walters, V. (1998) <u>Are We There Yet, Daddy?</u> New York: Viking. ISBN 0670874027

Willis, S. (2000). <u>Tell Me How Far It Is</u>. New York: Franklin Watts. ISBN 0531159752.

Willis, S. (1999). <u>Tell Me How Much It Weighs</u>. New York: Franklin Watts. ISBN 0531159779

Learning About Measurement

Name: _____

Introductory Activity 1

In the National Flea Jumping Contest, each flea's length of jump is marked below. Using a centimeter ruler, measure the distance that each flea jumped. Circle the flea that jumped the farthest.

Fred Flea _____ inches

Fanny Flea _____ inches

Fern Flea _____ inches

Frank Flea _____ inches

Francine Flea _____ inches

 Learning About Measurement

Name: _____

Introductory Activity 2

At Erin's birthday, everyone made their own ice cream sundaes! They each chose two different sauces. What is the total number of teaspoons (tsp) of sauce that each person put on their sundae? Write your answer on the blank.

Erin

5 tsp strawberry sauce
+ 6 tsp chocolate sauce

_____

Brian

7 tsp caramel sauce
+ 6 tsp chocolate sauce

_____

Hannah

9 tsp blueberry sauce
+ 5 tsp strawberry sauce

_____

Russell

6 tsp hot fudge sauce
+ 9 tsp chocolate sauce

_____

Dana

7 tsp pineapple sauce
+ 8 tsp butterscotch sauce

_____

Sean

8 tsp chocolate sauce
+ 6 tsp cherry sauce

_____

Learning About Measurement

Name: _____

Introductory Activity 3

Things can change their weight over time. Figure out the difference in weight (mass) in pounds. Write your answer on the blank.

Sarah weighed 7 pounds when she was born.

Sarah now weighs 55 pounds.

The difference in weight (mass) is _____ pounds.

The wheelbarrow filled with soil weighs 39 pounds.

After Mom did her gardening, the wheelbarrow weighed 11 pounds.

The difference in weight (mass) is _____ pounds.

Jessie's kitten was 3 pounds when she bought him.

Her cat weighed 9 pounds the next time the vet saw him.

The difference in weight (mass) is _____ pounds.

The restaurant owner bought 110 pounds of potatoes.

After the french fry eating contest was over, there were 13 pounds of potatoes.

The difference in weight (mass) is _____ pounds.

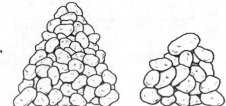

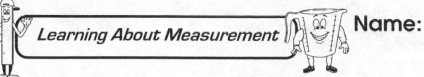

Learning About Measurement

Name: _____

Introductory Activity 4

Gina's class is having a Teddy Bear Picnic! Everyone brought a teddy bear. Jenna won the prize for the softest teddy bear. Ted won the prize for the best dressed teddy bear.

There were four people who had very small teddy bears. Measure the teddy bears below to determine who should win the prize for the smallest teddy bear.

Colleen's Bear

Ethan's Bear

Helen's Bear

Elisabeth's Bear

Learning About Measurement

Name: _____

Introductory Activity 5

Discover the mass or weight of each of the personal items listed below. Write the mass or weight in ounces.

1. your scissors: _____ ounces

2. a math book: _____ ounces

3. a toy: _____ ounces

4. your glue bottle: _____ ounces

5. a reading book: _____ ounces

6. a calculator: _____ ounces

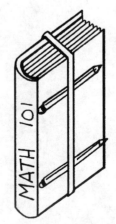

7. your shoe: _____ ounces

8. your pencil case: _____ ounces

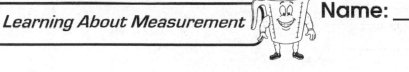

Name: _____

Introductory Activity 6

Rachel and Natalie are sisters. They argue about who has the biggest piece of pie. They argue about who made the biggest sand castle. They are always comparing their things.

Here are some things that they measured. Calculate the area of each item. Circle the picture of the girl that has the biggest area of each thing.

Rachel's poster of the "Lay-Z Boyz" group is _____ in.^{2}

(L = 8 in., W = 10 in.)

Natalie's poster of "Pop Princess" is _____ in.^{2}

(L = 9 inc., W = 9 in.)

Rachel's bedroom is _____ ft.^{2}

(L = 9 ft., W = 10 ft.)

Natalie's bedroom is _____ ft.^{2}

(L = 12 ft., W = 12 ft.)

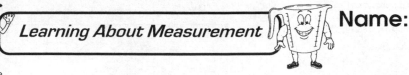

Learning About Measurement

Name: _____

Introductory Activity 7

While these friends were eating lunch, they wanted to know who had more in their drink. Compare the volume of the two friends' drinks. Circle the drink that has more volume.

1. Hunter's orange juice is 8 ounces

Vecepia's milk is 10 ounces

2. Roger's milkshake is 12 ounces

Teresa's grape juice is 6 ounces

3. Lindsey's apple juice is 15 ounces

Colby's cola is 12 ounces

4. Sonja's chocolate milk is 13 ounces

Joel's orange soda is 10 ounces

Learning About Measurement   Name: _____

Introductory Activity 8

Using a ruler, measure the length and width of each object. Write down the measurements on the lines provided.

Calculate the area of each shape.

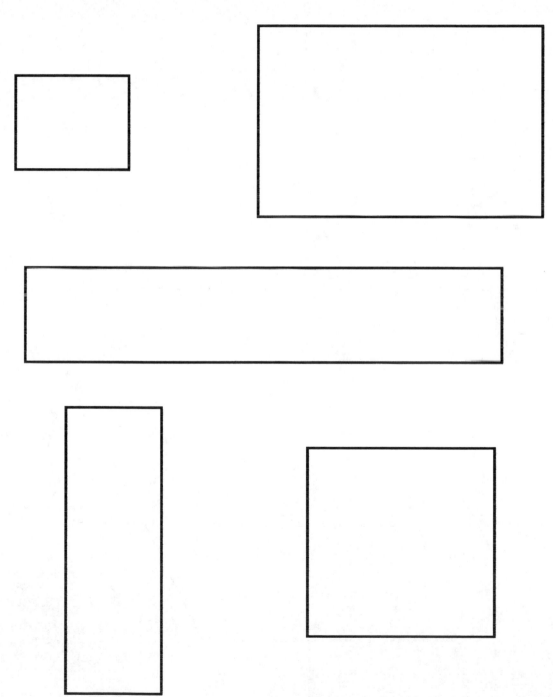

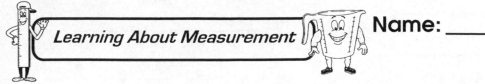

Learning About Measurement

Name: _____

Phonics Card 1

Rulers are used to measure the length of items or distances in inches.

Ruler begins with the letter "r". In the ruler below, print five words that begin with the letter "r".

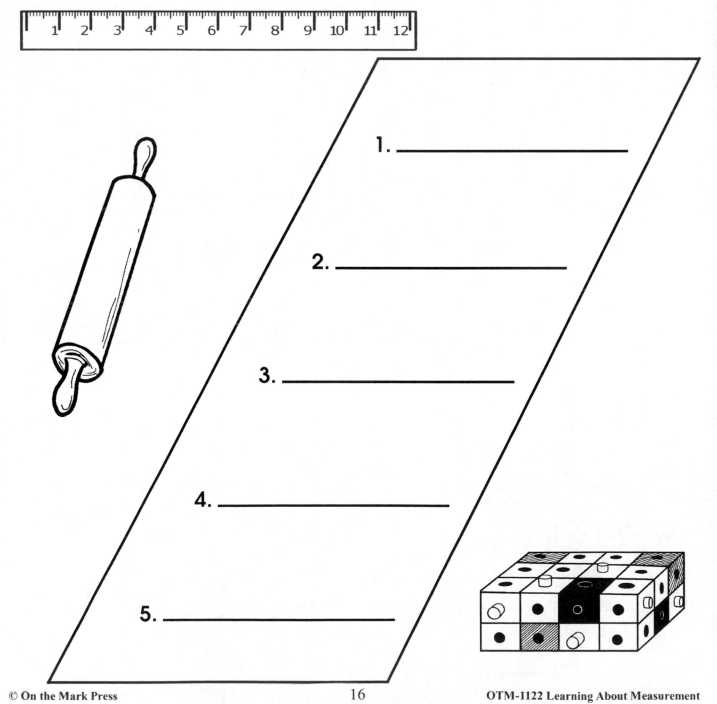

1. _____

2. _____

3. _____

4. _____

5. _____

Learning About Measurement

Name: _____

Phonics Card 2

Scales are used to weigh things to find out what their weight (mass) is.

Scale begins with the letter blend "sc".

In the scale below, draw pictures of five things that start with the letter blend "sc".

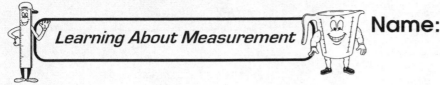

Learning About Measurement

Name: _____

Phonics Card 3

Capacity means how much a container can hold.

Capacity begins with the letter "c".

Read the words and the meanings below. Neatly print each word beside its correct meaning.

clown	coat	crayon	coffee	carpet
candy	Christmas	California	cube	calendar

1. a hot drink _____

2. a holiday in December _____

3. something to draw with _____

4. a sweet treat _____

5. a silly person with make-up and colorful clothes _____

6. something that covers the floor _____

7. has the days and months on it _____

8. something worn on cold days _____

9. a large state _____

10. a shape with six square sides _____

Learning About Measurement

Name: _____

Phonics Card 4

When we guess how long or how heavy something is, we are making an **estimate**.

Estimate begins with a "short e" sound.

Sound out each word and listen to the sound that the vowel makes. On the line beside each word, print "long" or "short".

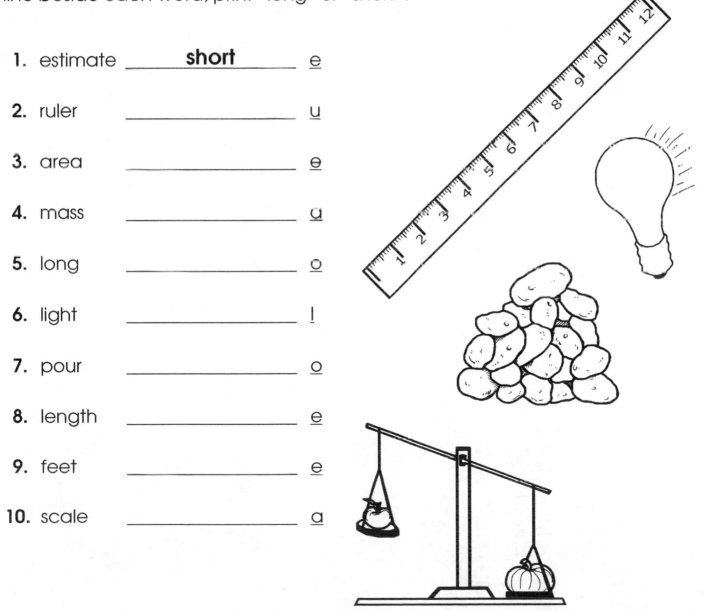

1. estimate _____**short**_____ e̲

2. ruler _____ u̲

3. area _____ e̲

4. mass _____ a̲

5. long _____ o̲

6. light _____ I̲

7. pour _____ o̲

8. length _____ e̲

9. feet _____ e̲

10. scale _____ a̲

OTM-1122 Learning About Measurement

Learning About Measurement

Name: _____

Word Study Card 1

We weigh things to find out what their **mass** is.

The heavier something is, the more its mass will be.

Mass rhymes with **pass**.

Neatly print a rhyming word for each of the words below.

1. light _____

2. weigh _____

3. cale _____

4. pound _____

5. weight _____

6. big _____

7. more _____

8. three _____

Learning About Measurement

Name: _____

Word Study Card 2

Length can be measured in inches.

Length tells us how long something is.

Length has **one syllable**.

Read the words below while clapping out the number of syllables that they have. Neatly print them under the proper heading.

| length | capacity | inch | foot | area |
| ruler | measure | miles | shorter | farthest |

1 Syllable	2 Syllables	3 Syllables	4 Syllables
length	_____	_____	_____
_____	_____		
_____	_____		
_____	_____		

Learning About Measurement

Name: _____

Word Study Card 3

Put the following **measurement** words in alphabetical order.

length	area	weigh	fill	pour	container
pound	cube	estimate	count	rulers	mile
balance					

1. _____
2. _____
3. _____
4. _____
5. _____
6. _____
7. _____
8. _____
9. _____
10. _____
11. _____
12. _____
13. _____

     OTM-1122 Learning About Measurement

Learning About Measurement   **Name:** _____

Word Study Card 4

Some things are **light** and some things are **heavy**.

Light and heavy are antonyms; they have opposite meanings.

Read each word and print the **antonym** beside it.

different	near	short	full	big
wide	fat	hard	young	day

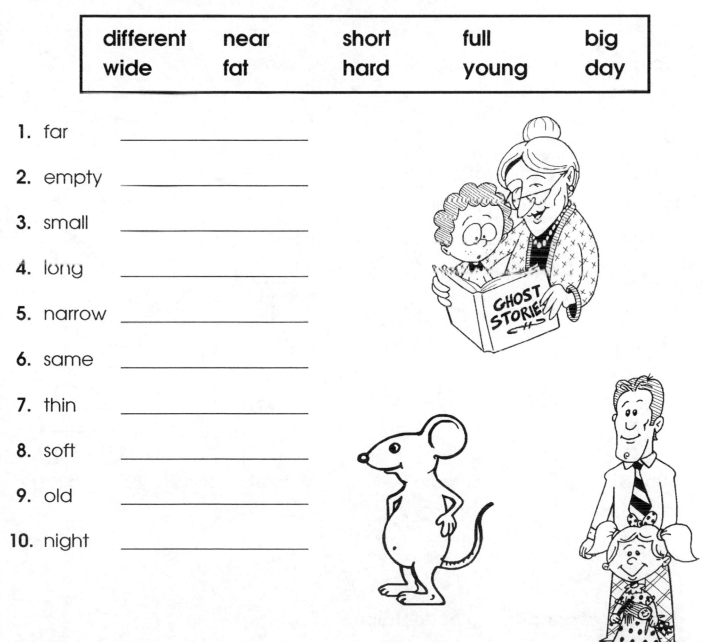

1. far _____

2. empty _____

3. small _____

4. long _____

5. narrow _____

6. same _____

7. thin _____

8. soft _____

9. old _____

10. night _____

23

Learning About Measurement   Name: _____

Word Study Card 5

Circle the words that are about **standard measurement**. (Do not circle words that could be used for non-standard measurements.)

1 cup

castle

scale

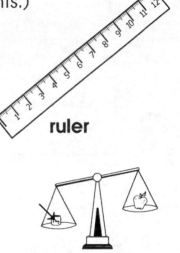
ruler

carrot

car

baby

pound

mass

gravy

girl

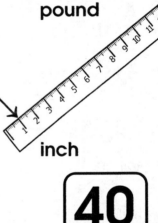
inch

ounce

table

quart carton

40 m.p.h. sign

1 ounce of pepper

heart shape

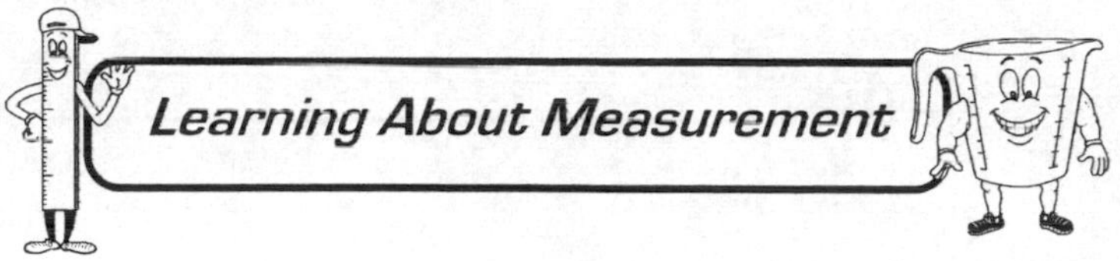

Learning About Measurement

Name: _____

Word Study Card 6

Use the set of words in one complete sentence.

| lighter | apple | watermelon |

1. _____

_____

| pencil | longer | toothpick |

2. _____

_____

| tea cup | milk carton | hold more |

3. _____

_____

| window | cover | curtains |

4. _____

_____

| I | heavier | teacher |

5. _____

_____

| bigger area | closet | bedroom |

6. _____

_____

Learning About Measurement

Name: _____

Linear Activity Card 1

Take three cube-a-links and put them together.

Find something in your classroom that is three cube-a-links long.

Trace the object that you have found.

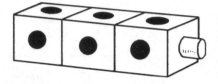

Trace an object that is the same length as one cube.

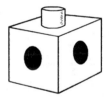

Trace an object that is five cube-a-links long.

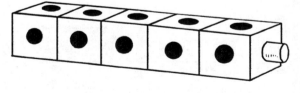

Name: _____

Linear Activity Card 2

Using one cube-a-link, **estimate** how many cubes long a piece of paper is.

I estimate my paper to be _____ cubes long.

Get enough cube-a-links to measure your paper.

My paper is _____ cubes long.

Learning About Measurement

Name: _____

Linear Activity Card 3

Color the pictures below of things that you would measure in **inches**.

Put an **X** through things that are **not** measured in inches.

pencil

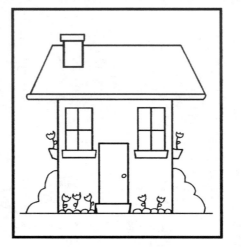

house

shoe

playground

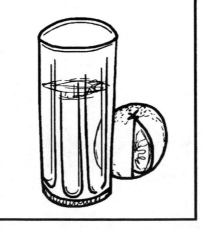

lemonade

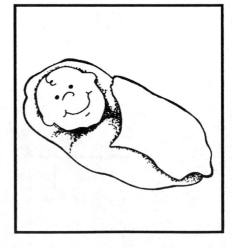

baby

Learning About Measurement

Name: _____

Linear Activity Card 4

Look at five different objects that your teacher has for you to measure (i.e. ruler, paper towel tube, can, book, pencil).

Estimate the order of the shortest to longest of the objects.

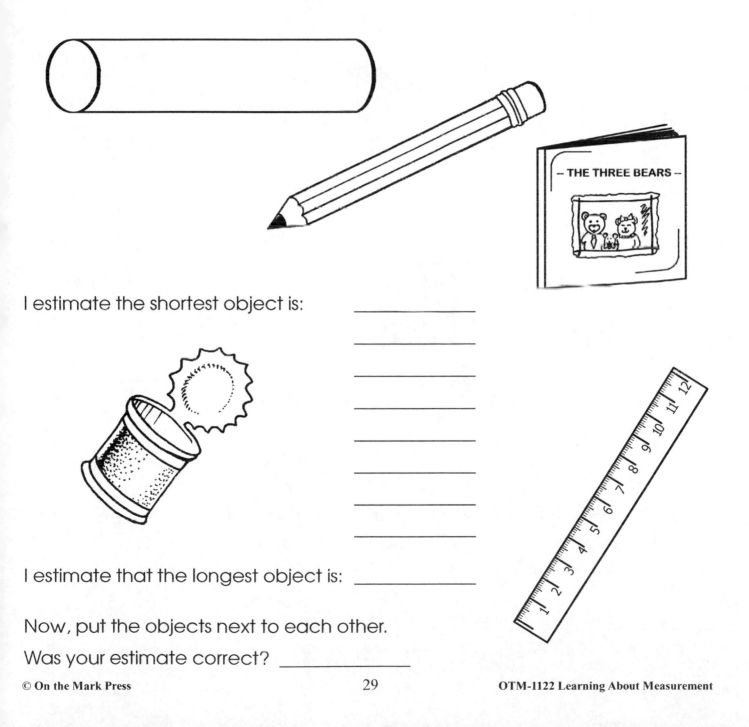

– THE THREE BEARS –

I estimate the shortest object is: _____

_____

_____

_____

_____

_____

_____

I estimate that the longest object is: _____

Now, put the objects next to each other.

Was your estimate correct? _____

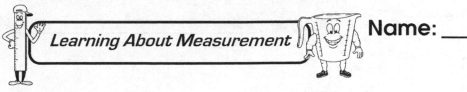

Name: _____

Linear Activity 5

Stand with your toes behind the piece of masking tape that your teacher has marked on the floor.

Take three regular steps. Put a piece of tape where your toe is. Using a yard stick, measure the distance that you walked.

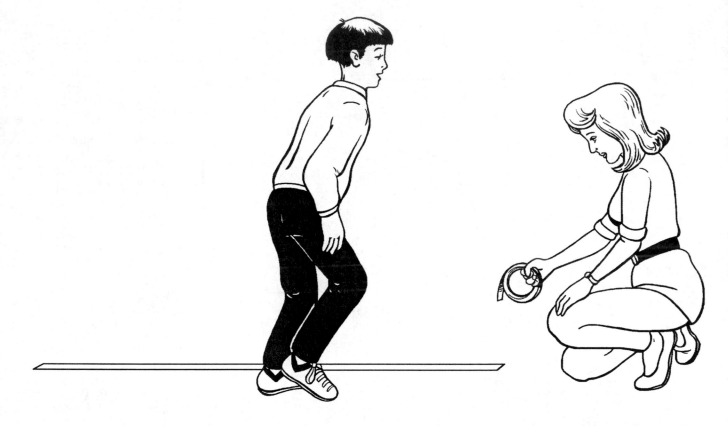

I walked _____ inches.

Record this distance on a class chart that your teacher made. When everyone has recorded how far they walked, figure out who walked the farthest and who walked the shortest distances.

_____ walked the farthest distance of _____ inches.

_____ walked the shortest distance of _____ inches.

Learning About Measurement

Name: _____

Linear Activity Card 6

Rulers are marked in inches and are used to measure lengths and distances. We can also measure lengths using other objects.

Trace your hand onto a piece of paper. Carefully cut it out. Use your "handprint" to see how long the following things are:

My teacher's desktop is _____ hands long.

My desk is _____ hands long.

My friend, _____, is _____ hands tall.

My leg is _____ hands long.

The distance from the door to the pencil sharpener is _____ hands.

Trace your hand and use scissors to cut it out.

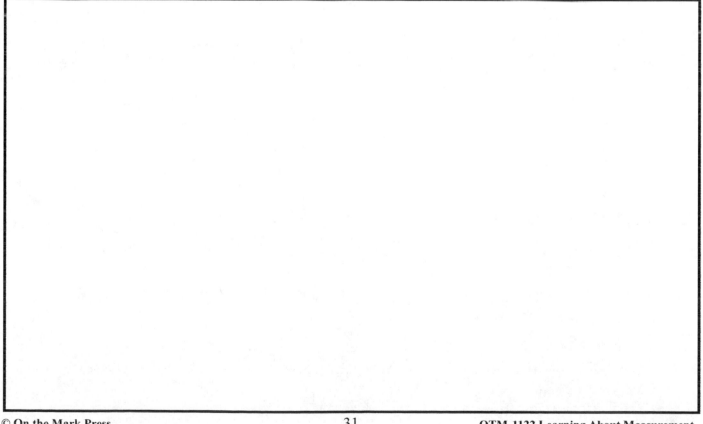

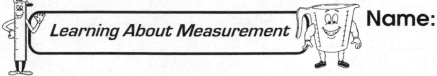

Learning About Measurement   **Name:** _____

Linear Activity Card 7

Some things are hard to measure with a straight stick.

1. Estimate and record how long you think each of the lines on this page are.

   Place a piece of string over these lines. Then straighten out the string and place it on top of a yard stick. Record how many inches each of these lines are:

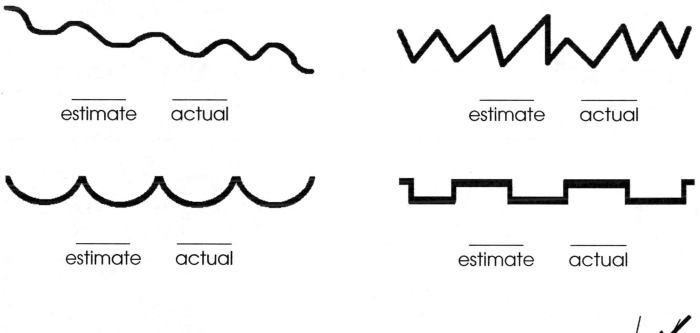

estimate   actual   estimate   actual

estimate   actual   estimate   actual

2. Use the string and yard stick to find out big your ankle is.
   My ankle is _____ inches around.

3. Find something in your classroom that is hard to measure with a ruler. Use a string to help find out how long it is.

   In my classroom, the _____ is _____ inches long.

Learning About Measurement

Name: _____

Linear Activity Card 8

Pick a partner and estimate each other's height.

I think that _____ is _____ in. tall.

Next, measure your partner's height in inches.

My partner is _____ in. tall.

Get a thin strip of paper, such as adding machine tape, from your teacher. Cut the paper to be as many inches as your partner is. Print your partner's name and height on the paper, i.e. Krista 42 inches.

The whole class can help put everyone's paper with their height on it, in order from shortest to tallest.

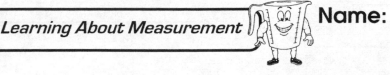

Name: _____

Linear Activity Card 9

You will need about five different balls (for example, tennis ball, baseball, basketball, golf ball, soccer ball) and a measuring tape.

The **circumference** is the measurement around the middle of the ball at its biggest part.

Estimate the order of the **circumference** of the balls, from smallest to largest.

I think the ball with the smallest circumference is: _____

_____
_____
_____
_____
_____

I think the ball with the largest circumference is: _____

Carefully measure the circumference around the middle of the ball. Record your answers.

The **smallest** circumference is _____ in. for the _____ ball.
The next smallest circumference is _____ in. for the _____ ball.
The next smallest circumference is _____ in. for the _____ ball.
The next smallest circumference is _____ in. for the _____ ball.
The **biggest** circumference is _____ in. for the _____ ball.

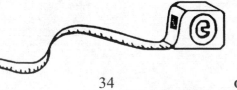

Learning About Measurement   **Name:** _____

Linear Activity Card 10

Read the sentence carefully.

Circle the best answer.

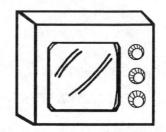

1. David needs a new hedge along one side of his walkway. What should he do?

    a) Find the area of the walkway.

    b) Find the mass or weight of the hedge.

    c) Find the length of the walkway.

2. Cameron wants to put his television five yards from his couch. What should he do?

    a) Measure the distance from his television with a yard stick.

    b) Watch the news on TV.

    c) Find the mass or weight of his TV.

3. Nicole wants to set up a basketball net three yards up a pole. What should she do?

    a) Find the mass or weight of the basketball.

    b) Use a yard stick to find where three yards above the ground is.

    c) Find the area of the basketball court.

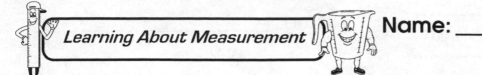

Learning About Measurement   Name: _____

Area Activity Card 1

There are many things at home and at school that **cover** other things.   The grass covers the field. Make a list of other things that cover.

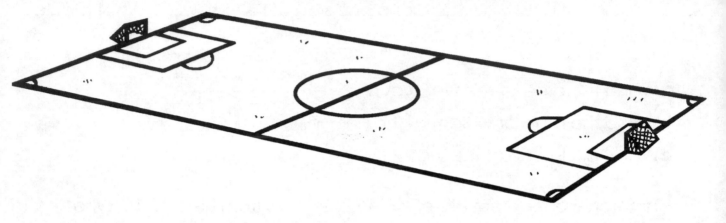

sheets cover my bed
_____

grass covers the school field
_____

_____

_____

_____

_____

_____

_____

Learning About Measurement Name: _____

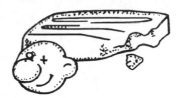

Area Activity Card 2

Fill an 8 ounce measuring cup with playdough.

Look at two different cookie cutter shapes. Guess which one will make more "cookies" from the playdough.

Trace the two shapes of the cookie cutters here:

Put a check beside the one that you think will make **more**. (**Hint:** the smaller one will make more cookies.)

Roll out the playdough. Stamp as many "cookie" shapes onto the playdough. Remember to have your cookies right beside each other in neat rows. Count the cookies and put that number in the shape of the cookie cutter that you traced on this paper.

Roll the dough back into a ball. Stamp out the "cookies" with the other shape. Count the shapes and print that number in the other shape that you traced.

Which shape stamped out more cookies? Circle that shape.

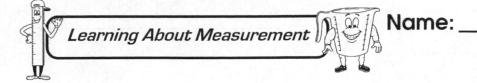
Learning About Measurement   **Name:** _____

Area Activity Card 3

Color the pictures below of things that you would measure in **yards squared.**

Put an **X** through things that are **not** measured in yd.²

carpet   tea   kitchen

spoon   curtains   rice

Learning About Measurement   **Name:** _____

Area Activity Card 4

Look at the two shapes below. Guess which shape is bigger. The shape that is bigger is the one that has a bigger **area**.   Put a check mark beside the shape that you think is bigger.

Cover both shapes with cube-a-links. Put as many cubes inside each shape that will fit, so that none of the shape is showing.

Count the cubes on each shape to figure out which one has the bigger **area**. Circle the shape that fit more cubes inside.

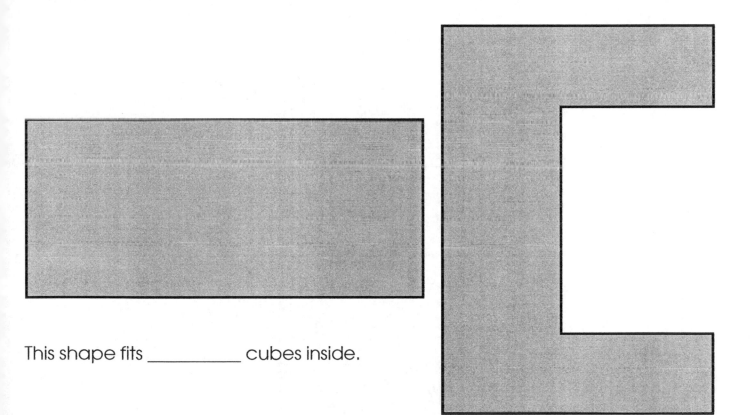

This shape fits _____ cubes inside.

This shape fits _____ cubes inside.

Learning About Measurement

Name: _____

Area Activity Card 5

Carefully cut out this shape along the lines. Then, put it back together. Put the pieces in an envelope and print "house" on it.

Make your own puzzle by drawing a simple shape. Using a ruler, draw a few lines in it. Cut out the puzzle pieces along the lines. Put it back together and carefully trace along the outline of your whole shape. Let your partner figure out how to put the pieces together into the shape that you made. Put all those pieces into a labeled envelope.

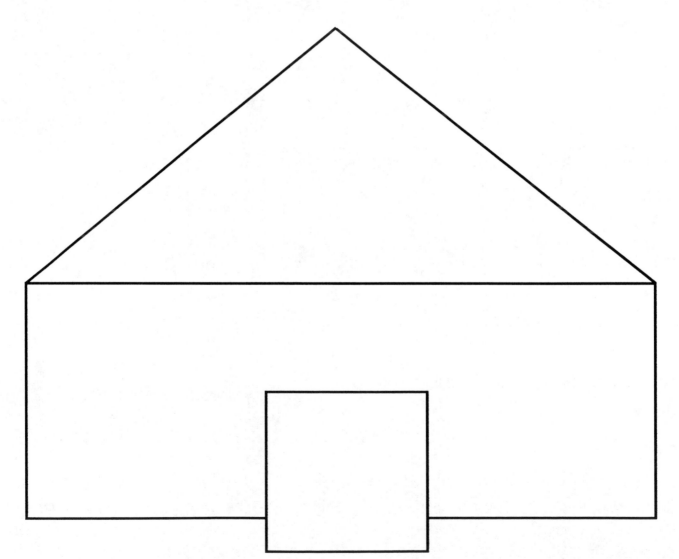

Name: _____

Area Activity Card 6

Arrange some pattern blocks in the top half of the grid below. Carefully trace around your shape.

Make a different shape in the bottom half of the grid. Trace around that shape.

Which shape do you think has a bigger **area**? Put a check mark beside the shape that you think is bigger.

Count the little squares inside each shape and record the number of squares that each shape has. This is the area of your shape. Circle the shape with the bigger area.

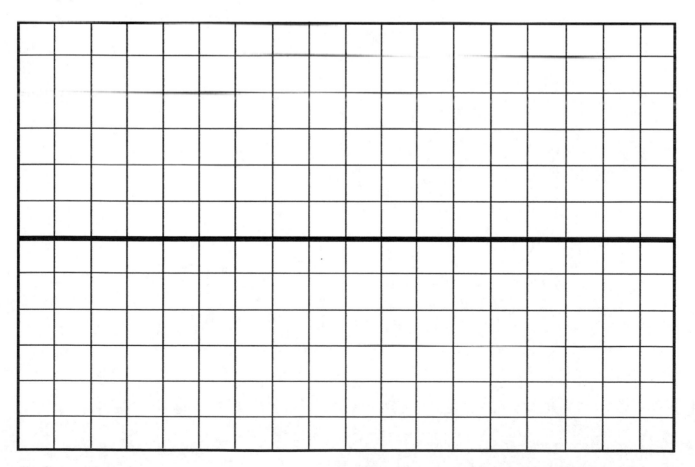

Learning About Measurement

Name: _____

Area Activity Card 7

The **area** of something is how much it takes to cover it. **Estimate** how many of a certain thing it would take to cover the items listed below. Then check how many it actually does take to cover the items.

I guess that it will take _____ cubes to cover my book.

It took _____ cubes to cover my book.

I guess that it will take _____ books to cover my desk.

It took _____ books to cover my desk.

I guess that it will take _____ pieces of paper to cover a table.

It took _____ pieces of paper to cover a table.

Learning About Measurement **Name:** _____

Area Activity Card 8

A square **yard** (yd.^{2}) is used to measure **area**.

We can use a **yard stick** to measure a table top. Measure two sides that are touching each other. Multiply those two numbers together. The answer is the area in y^2.

Example: 3 yd.→

2 yd.↓ $3 \times 2 = 6$

This table top is 6 yd.^{2}.

Estimate and then use a meter stick to **measure** the following things:

Table top

Estimate: _____ yd.^{2} Actual: _____ yd.^{2}

Classroom floor

Estimate: _____ yd.^{2} Actual: _____ yd.^{2}

Bulletin board

Estimate: _____ yd.^{2} Actual: _____ yd.^{2}

Classroom door

Estimate: _____ yd.^{2} Actual: _____ yd.^{2}

_____
      (your choice)

Estimate: _____ yd.^{2} Actual: _____ yd.^{2}

Learning About Measurement

Name: _____

Area Activity Card 9

To measure things that are smaller than a yard, we use **square inches** (in.²).

We can use a **ruler** to measure a piece of paper. Measure two sides that are touching each other. Multiply those two numbers together. The answer is the area in in.².

Example: 4 in.→ 2 in.↓

$4 \times 2 = 8$

This paper is 8 in.².

Estimate and then use a ruler to **measure** the following things:

Paper

Estimate: _____ in.²   Actual: _____ in.²

Story book

Estimate: _____ in.²   Actual: _____ in.²

One side of box

Estimate: _____ in.²   Actual: _____ in.²

Envelope

Estimate: _____ in.²   Actual: _____ in.²

_____
     (**your choice**)

Estimate: _____ in.²   Actual: _____ in.²

-- THE THREE BEARS --

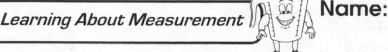 Learning About Measurement  **Name:** _____

Area Activity Card 10

1. Paige wants new carpet for her den. What should she do?

   a) Lie down in her den.
   b) Find the area of her den.
   c) Walk across her den.

2. Robert wants to buy a tablecloth for a rectangular table. What should he do?

   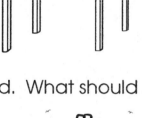

   a) Find the mass or weight of the table.
   b) Find the length of the table.
   c) Measure the length and width of the table.

3. James is going to cover the new playground with sand. What should he do first?

   a) Find the area of the playground.
   b) Build a sandcastle with 8 ounce containers.
   c) Compare which bucket holds more sand.

4. Jasdeep's father is going to buy paper to put on her paint easel. How will he know what size of paper to buy?

   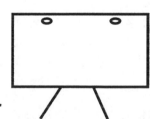

   a) Ask Jasdeep what size of picture she likes to draw.
   b) Measure the length and width of the easel.
   c) Measure how much paint Jasdeep's paint cans hold.

5. Dalia wants to make a picture frame for her mom's birthday. How will Dalia know what size of frame to make?

   a) Measure the length and width of the picture.
   b) Choose the best paper for a picture frame.
   c) Ask her mom what her favorite picture is.

Learning About Measurement

Name: _____

Weight Activity Card 1

Pick six different objects in your classroom (make sure that the objects are small enough to fit on the scale in your classroom).

Pick them up and guess which one is the lightest, the middle weight, and the heaviest.

Print the names of the objects in the order that you estimate their weight or mass from lightest to heaviest.

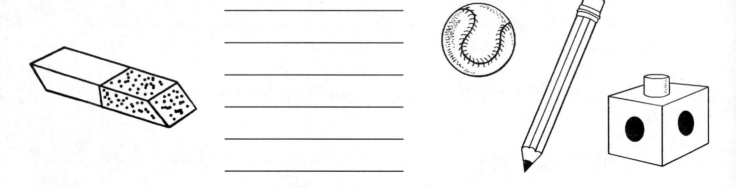

_____

_____

_____

_____

_____

_____

Weigh each object on the scale. Record the weight or mass and list them in order from lightest to heaviest.

The _____ has a weight (mass) of _____ ounces.

The _____ has a weight (mass) of _____ ounces.

The _____ has a weight (mass) of _____ ounces.

The _____ has a weight (mass) of _____ ounces.

The _____ has a weight (mass) of _____ ounces.

The _____ has a weight (mass) of _____ ounces.

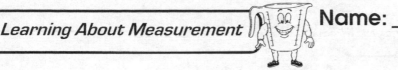

Learning About Measurement **Name:** _____

Weight Activity Card 2

We can use **ounces** to weigh objects. We can also use other objects to compare the weight (mass) of different objects.

Choose cube-a-links, popsicle sticks, legos, or something else that your teacher has provided.

Estimate how many of your chosen objects will equal the weight (mass) of each object listed below.

Object	Estimate	Actual
my calculator =	100 cube-a-links	123 cube-a-links
my pencil =		
chalkboard eraser =		
my eraser =		
tennis ball =		
scissors =		
a notebook =		

Now using the scale, check your estimates. Place the first item (pencil) on one side of the scale and start putting the objects (i.e. cubes) on the other side until the scale is balanced. Count the number of objects that it took to balance the scale. Record your answers.

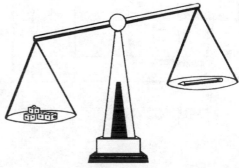

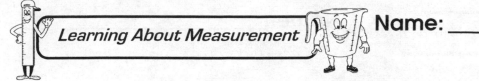

Learning About Measurement

Name: _____

Weight Activity Card 3

Color the pictures below of things that you would measure in **ounces**.

Put an **X** through things that are <u>not</u> measured in ounces.

cereal   **juice**   **macaroni**

packages   **milk**   **bedspread**

Learning About Measurement

Name: _____

Weight Activity Card 4

A **pound** (lb.) is used to measure **weight** (**mass**).

Pick up a one pound weight (mass). Hold it in one hand and try to remember how heavy it is.

Now pick up your shoe. Do you think your shoe weighs more or less than 1 lb.?

Record your guess on the chart below.

Then, weigh your shoe and record the actual weight (mass). Was your guess correct?

Do this for each item listed in the chart. (Choose five more objects for the blank spaces.)

Object	My Guess (more or less than 1 lb.)	Actual Weight (mass)
my shoe		
stapler		
3 hole punch		
text book		

Learning About Measurement   **Name:** _____

Weight Activity Card 5

Pick up a **one pound weight** (**mass**) in one hand.

Pick up one piece of fruit or vegetable in the other hand.

Guess how many of that fruit it will take to equal 1 pound.

Use a scale to find out the actual answer. Record the results.

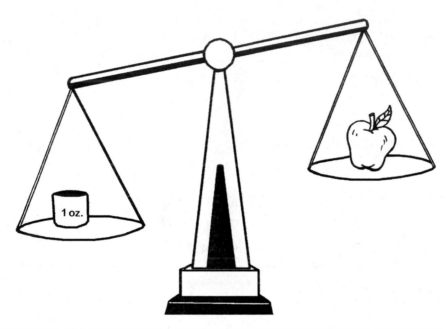

Fruit or Vegetable	Number to make about 1 pound
orange	
potato	
cob of corn	
banana	
apple	

Learning About Measurement

Name: _____

Weight Activity Card 6

Lighter objects are weighed in **ounces**.

Hold a one ounce weight (mass) in one hand.

Pick up an object that you think has a weight (mass) of about one ounce.

Use a scale to check if the object actually does weigh one ounce.

List the items that you checked on the chart below:

< 1 oz. (less than 1 oz.)	1 oz. (exactly 1 oz.)	> 1 oz. (more than 1 oz.)
1.		
2.		
3.		
4.		
5.		
6.		
7.		
8.		
9.		
10.		

Name: _____

Weight Activity Card 7

Look at the containers filled with pasta, rice, cereal and sand.

Without picking them up, guess which one is the lightest and which one is the heaviest.

Pick each one up. Do you want to change any of your guesses?

I think the lightest thing is the   _____

_____

_____

_____

I think the heaviest thing is the   _____

Use a scale to find the actual weight (mass) of each container.

Record the results.

The _____ has a weight (mass) of _____ ounces.

The _____ has a weight (mass) of _____ ounces.

The _____ has a weight (mass) of _____ ounces.

The _____ has a weight (mass) of _____ ounces.

The _____ has a weight (mass) of _____ ounces.

Learning About Measurement

Name: _____

Weight Activity Card 8

Do you think air has weight?

Tape three empty balloons to a balance. Record the weight.

Blow up the three balloons. Using the piece of tape, attach the three balloons to the balance again. Record the weight (mass).

The empty balloons had a weight (mass) of _____ ounces.

The full balloons had a weight (mass) of _____ ounces.

Discuss the answer with a partner.

Name: _____

Weight Activity Card 9

Choose six objects from the classroom.

Fill in the graph below with the names of the objects across the bottom row and the possible weights (mass) in the first column.

Estimate the weight (mass) of each one. Record your estimate in **blue** on the graph.

Find the actual weight (mass) of each object. Record the actual results in **red** on the graph.

_____ oz.						
_____ oz.						
_____ oz.						
_____ oz.						
_____ oz.						
_____ oz.						
Weight	book					

Learning About Measurement   Name: _____

Weight Activity Card 10

1. Stephanie wants to find out how many stamps she needs for her package. What should she do?

   a) Put the package on one side of a balance scale and some stamps on the other side.
   b) Find the weight (mass) of the package.
   c) Measure the distance from her house to the post office.

2. Mrs. Blackburn needs a 20 pound turkey for the holiday dinner. What should she do?

   a) Find the weight (mass) of the turkey in the store.
   b) Find the weight (mass) of all the people in the family.
   c) Find the area of the dinner table.

3. Amanda needs to weigh some tomatoes for a recipe. What should she use?

   a) ruler
   b) yard stick
   c) scale

4. Dr. Wong needs to find out if Baby Jake gained weight since his last visit. Last week, Jake had a weight of 8 lb. Today Jake has a weight of 160 oz. What happened?

   a) Jake gained weight.
   b) Jake lost weight.
   c) Jake's weight stayed the same.

5. After returning from trick-or-treating on Halloween night, Chiara and Rod each weighed their Halloween bags. Chiara's had a weight (mass) of 6.0 lb. while Rod's had a weight (mass) of 80 oz. Who had the heaviest bag?

   a) Chiara
   b) Rod
   c) They were both equal.

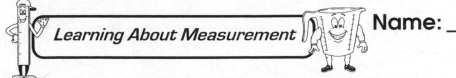

Name: _____

Volume and Capacity Activity Card 1

Containers are used to hold many different things (juice, paint, rice, blocks, etc.)

Look through a magazine and cut out pictures of **containers**.

Make a collage.

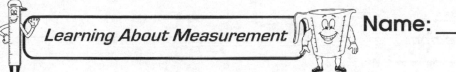

Learning About Measurement   Name: _____

Volume and Capacity Activity Card 2

Capacity is how much a container can hold.

Look at two containers of different size and shape. Which do you think will hold more sand?

Fill the one that you think holds **less** to the top with sand.

Next, pour that sand into the other container. Did it all fit?

Record your findings.

SAND

I think the container with this shape _____ will hold more.

My guess was correct/incorrect.

Name: _____

Volume and Capacity Activity Card 3

Color the pictures below of things that you would measure in **ounces**.

Put an **X** through things that are **<u>not</u>** measured in oz.

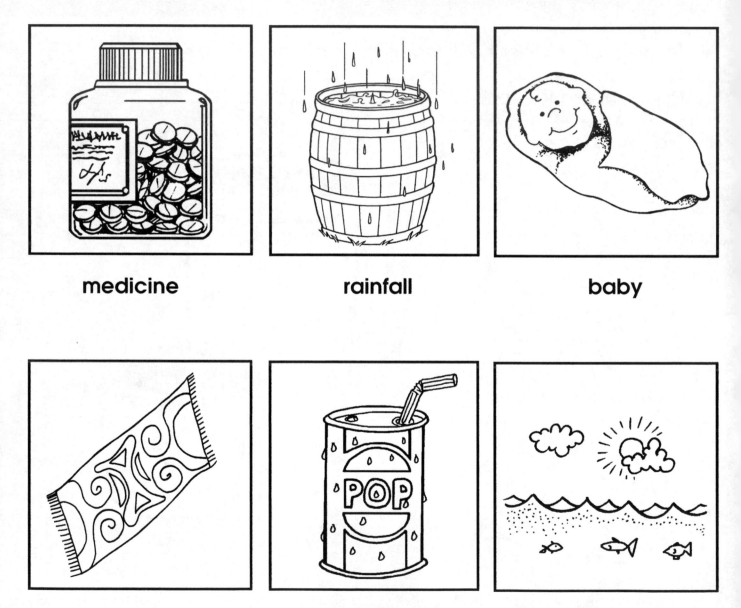

medicine	rainfall	baby

carpet	pop in can	ocean

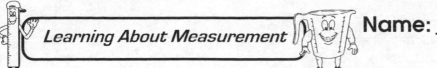

Name: _____

Volume and Capacity Activity Card 4

Choose two different containers and guess which one holds more. Guess how many small cups of sand will be needed to fill each one.

Using a small cup (e.g. dixie cup), fill each container until it is full.

Record how many cupfuls it took to fill each one.

Example:

It took 12 cups to fill this container.

It took 16 cups to fill this container.

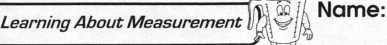

Learning About Measurement

Name: _____

Volume and Capacity Activity Card 5

A **quart** (qt.) is used to measure **capacity**.

Look at a quart container. Compare other containers to the quart container and guess which ones hold more or less than 1 quart..

Fill the quart container with water and carefully pour the water into another container.

Draw the shapes of the containers in the proper place below, depending on if they were able to hold all of the water from the quart container or not.

<1 qt. (holds less than 1 quart) =1 qt. (holds exactly 1 quart) >1 qt. (holds more than 1 quart)

Name: _____

Volume and Capacity Activity Card 6

Look at two different sizes of empty boxes and guess which one holds more.

Estimate how many cube-a-links it would take to fill each box.

Record your guesses.

I think it will take _____ cubes to fill the smaller box.

I think it will take _____ cubes to fill the larger box.

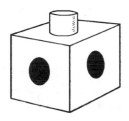

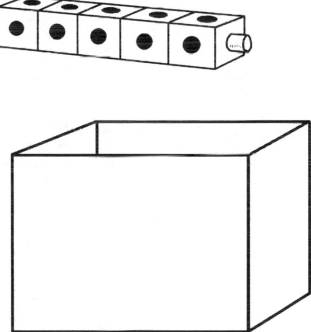

Fill each box and record the actual answers.

It took _____ cubes to fill the box that I thought was smaller.

It took _____ cubes to fill the box that I thought was larger.

Learning About Measurement

Name: _____

Volume and Capacity Activity Card 7

Build a **rectangular prism** using cubes. Guess how many cubes you used.

I think I used _____ cubes to make my rectangular prism.

Next, count how many cubes you actually used.

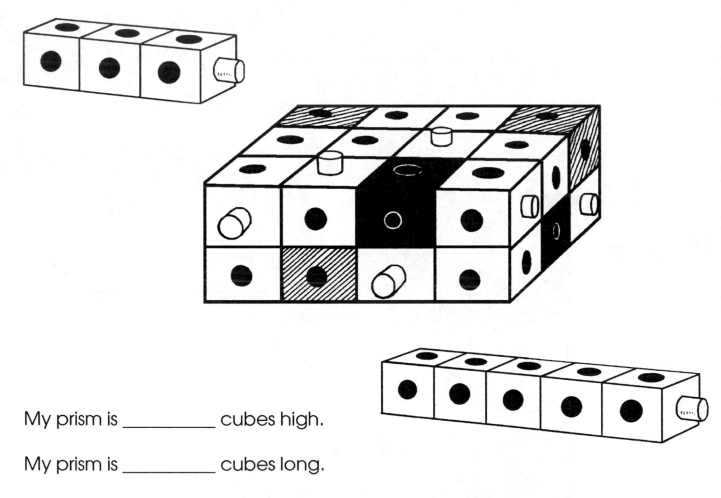

My prism is _____ cubes high.

My prism is _____ cubes long.

My prism is _____ cubes deep.

You will need to take your prism apart to count each cube now.

I used a total of _____ cubes to make my rectangular prism.

 **Learning About Measurement**

Name: _____

Volume and Area Activity Card 8

Find one or two partners.

Gather newspaper, scissors, masking tape, rulers and yard sticks, cardboard (and something to cut it with), and markers.

Think of a way to build models of square inches, square yards, and then cubic inches, and cubic yards.

Label the models.

When you have finished, share your models with the class. Tell them what you have built, what it is called, and how it compares with some of the other models built by other groups.

Learning About Measurement

Name: _____

Volume and Capacity Card 9

In this activity, you will need a plastic cup to measure the capacity of larger items and an eye dropper to measure the capacity of smaller items.

Choose which unit of measure you will need for the first item. Estimate how many of that unit you will need to fill the item. Record your estimate.

Measure the actual capacity by filling the cup with water and pouring it into the item, or by filling the eye dropper with water and squirting it into the item. Count as you go along and record the actual measurement.

Item Measured	√ if using eye dropper	√ if using a cup	My Estimate	Actual Measurement
pail				
milk carton				
spoon				
baby food jar				
bowl				

Learning About Measurement

Name: _____

Volume and Capacity Activity Card 10

1. Mary Beth needs to buy a quart of milk. What should she do?

   a) Use a ruler to find the length of a carton.

   b) Find out which carton has the same weight (mass) as three potatoes.

   c) Look at the milk carton to see which one says 1 qt.

2. Laura needs to measure some salt for a recipe. What should she use?

   a) measuring spoon

   b) scale

   c) 1 ounce

3. Daniel needs about 8 ounces of soil to fill his flowerpot. What should he use to carry the soil from the garden to his deck?

   a) large pail

   b) spoon

   c) cup

4. Ken wants to know how much water is in his birdbath. What units will he use to measure the water?

   a) cubic yards

   b) quarts

   c) inches squared

5. Josiah needs 17 oz. of milk and 15 oz. of water for a recipe. How much liquid is in the recipe?

   a) 2 quarts

   b) 4 cups

   c) 1 pint

Learning About Measurement

Matching Activity Card 1

Teacher instructions: Glue this page to a sturdy backing. Laminate. Cut along the lines. Put pieces into an envelope and attach instructions.

Match the correct word to the proper sentences.	
I am used to measure how long something is. I am marked in inches. I have a straight edge. **What am I?**	**scale**
You can fill me with water, sand, juice or rice. You can pour things out of me. I can be marked in ounces or cups. **What am I?**	**ruler**
I am used to find out what weight things have. I am in your bathroom, doctor's office, post office, butcher shop. You read my numbers in ounces or pounds. **What am I?**	**mile**
You need to find me if you want to buy carpet for the floor. You need to find me if you want to put up new wallpaper. You need to find me if you want to get a new tablecloth. I am measured in in². **What am I?**	**area**
I am 1,760 yards. I am used to measure how far away places are. My short form is mi. **What am I?**	**container**

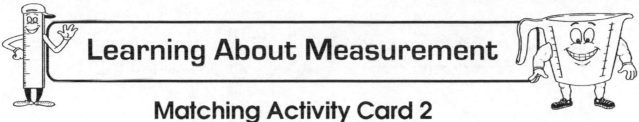

Learning About Measurement

Matching Activity Card 2

Teacher instructions: Glue this page to a sturdy backing. Laminate. Cut along the lines. Put pieces into an envelope and attach instructions.

Match the picture to the correct word.

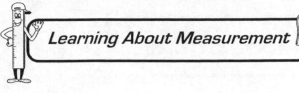 **Learning About Measurement**

Name: _____

Creative Writing Card 1

Think about a job where you would need to measure the length of things (i.e. construction worker, doctor, architect, seamstress, decorator, builder). Write about a day on the job for one of these people. Be sure to write about what they measured and what happens if they make a mistake.

_____

_____

_____

_____

_____

_____

_____

_____

_____

_____

_____

_____

_____

_____

_____

_____

_____

_____

_____

Learning About Measurement

Name: _____

Creative Writing Card 2

Think about a job where people weigh things (i.e., doctor, butcher, truck weigh stations, grocery store, post office, etc.). What things are weighed? Are they weighed in ounces, pounds or both?

Make a **story** about a day on the job in one of these places. Be sure to include details about what is being weighed!

_____

_____

_____

_____

_____

_____

_____

_____

_____

_____

_____

_____

_____

_____

_____

Learning About Measurement

Name: _____

Creative Writing Card 3

Make a sentence for each of the following words:

fill   pour   full   empty   container

1. _____

2. _____

3. _____

4. _____

5. _____

Learning About Measurement

Name: _____

Creative Writing Card 4

Write a story about something that you needed to "cover". (It can be real or an imaginary story.) Did you need to spread some sand around a playground or buy some material to sew some placemats? Explain how you figured out how much of the "cover" to buy and what you "covered".

_____

_____

_____

_____

_____

_____

_____

_____

_____

_____

_____

_____

_____

_____

_____

_____

_____

_____

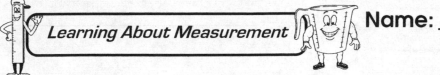 **Learning About Measurement**

Name: _____

Creative Writing Card 5

When traveling, maps are very important. They show where to go and how far to travel along each road.

Write a story about a family using a map while on vacation.

_____

_____

_____

_____

_____

_____

_____

_____

_____

_____

_____

_____

_____

_____

_____

_____

_____

_____

_____

Learning About Measurement

Name: _____

Reading Activity Card 1

Read <u>How Big Is A Foot?</u> by Rolf Myller.

Answer the questions in complete sentences.

1. What did the King order for the Queen?

   _____

2. How did the King measure the size of the bed he wanted?

   _____

3. What size of bed did the King ask for?

   _____

4. Why was the bed too small?

   _____

5. Why do you think that the ruler was invented?

   _____

6. Draw a picture of your favorite part of the story.

Learning About Measurement   **Name:** _____

Reading Activity Card 2

Read <u>The Very Hungry Caterpillar</u> by Eric Carle.

1. What did the caterpillar eat?

   _____
   _____
   _____
   _____

2. List the foods that the caterpillar ate from what you think is the lightest to the heaviest in weight.

   _____
   _____
   _____
   _____

3. List the foods in alphabetical order.

   _____
   _____
   _____

4. Draw a picture of your favorite food.

 **Learning About Measurement** **Name:** _____

Math Activity Card 1

1. What does in. mean? _____

2. What does yd. mean? _____

3. What does mi. mean? _____

4. What is the short form (abbreviation) for inch?

   _____

5. What is the short form (abbreviation) for yard?

   _____

6. What is the short form for mile?

   _____

7. How many inches are equal to one yard?

   _____

8. How many yards are equal to 1 mile?

   _____

9. Name one thing that can be measured in inches.

   _____

10. Name one thing that can be measured in yards.

    _____

11. Name one thing that can be measured in miles.

    _____

Learning About Measurement

Name: _____

Math Activity Card 2

1. What does pt. stand for?

   _____

2. What does qt. stand for?

   _____

3. What is the short form (abbreviation) for ounce?

   _____

4. What is the short form for quart?

   _____

5. How many ounces are equal to one quart?

   _____

6. Name one thing that can be measured in ounces.

   _____

7. Name one thing that can be measured in quarts.

   _____

8. How many oz. are equal to 2.0 qts.?

   _____

9. Define **capacity**.

   _____

10. How many cups are equal to 80 oz.?

    _____

Learning About Measurement   Name: _____

Math Activity Card 3

1. What does oz. stand for?

_____

2. What does lb. stand for?

_____

3. What is the short form (abbreviation) for ounce?

_____

4. What is the short form for pound?

_____

5. How many ounces are equal to 1 pound?

_____

6. How many inches are equal to 1 yard?

_____

7. Name one thing that can be measured in ounces.

_____

8. Name one thing that can be measured in pounds.

_____

9. What do we use to find the weight of things?

_____

Learning About Measurement

Name: _____

Math Activity Card 4

1. Jenny left her classroom and walked five yards to the drinking fountain and then ten yards to the washroom. How far did Jenny walk?

   _____
   _____
   _____

2. Paula, Marc and Ellen were having a contest to see who could throw a baseball the farthest. Paula threw the ball 42 yards. Marc threw the ball 49 yards and Ellen threw the ball 25 yards. List the children in order from the shortest to the farthest throwers.

   _____
   _____
   _____

3. When Mom and Mandeep drove to Grandma's, Mom drove 500 yards to the grocery store and then continued another 800 yards to Grandma's. Later, Mom drove straight home for 1 mile. Which trip was longer, the one going to Grandma's or the one coming home from Grandma's and by how much?

   _____
   _____
   _____

4. Constance is 48 in. tall. Joelle is 36 in. tall. How much taller is Constance?

   _____
   _____
   _____

5. Sabrina weighed all her birthday presents before she opened them. The present from Kelly had a weight of 2 lbs.. Dorothy's present had a weight of 32 oz.. The gift that Heather brought had a weight of 1 lb. List the presents in order from lightest to heaviest.

   _____
   _____
   _____

Learning About Measurement   **Name:** _____

Math Activity Card 5

1. Put these items in order from what you think will be the lightest to the heaviest: orange, balloon, soccer ball, computer, pencil.

_____

_____

_____

2. Joyce bought mixed nuts for a party. She bought 8 ounces of peanuts, 16 ounces of walnuts and 6 ounces of cashews. How many grams of nuts did Joyce buy?

_____

_____

3. Adam went to the store and bought a 2 qt. bottle of orange juice and a 1 qt. carton of milk. How many quarts did Adam buy?

_____

_____

4. Diego bought 10 oz. of strawberry yogurt and 30 oz. of peach yogurt. Annette bought 1 qt. of cherry yogurt. Who bought more yogurt?

_____

_____

5. When Melanie was moving, she had three boxes of the same size and shape. In one box, she packed 15 books of the same size. In another box, she packed 20 videos. In the third box, she packed four stuffed toys of the same size. Can you figure out which item was the biggest and which was the smallest of her books, videos and toys?

_____

_____

_____

Learning About Measurement   Name: _____

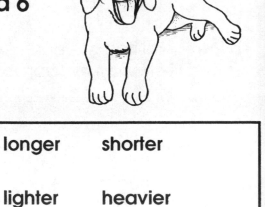

Math Activity Card 6

This is Lady and her puppy, Trixie.

Circle the correct answer.

1. Is Trixie longer or shorter than her mom?	**longer** **shorter**
2. Is Trixie lighter or heavier than her mom?	**lighter** **heavier**
3. Who is taller?	**Trixie** **Lady**
4. How long is Trixie?	**24 in.** **24 yards**
5. In which unit of measurement would you find Trixie's weight?	**gallons** **pounds** **yards**

Color the picture.

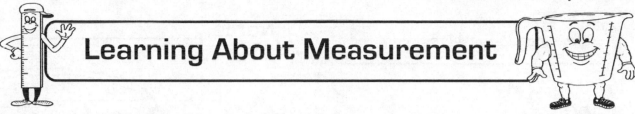

Learning About Measurement

Note to Teachers: This activity can be done as a class with early primary students. Discuss the measurements that are being used, the filling of the various measurement containers and the area that the pizza is taking up. For some older students, you may wish to allow small groups to measure out their own ingredients and toppings. They can also compare the differences in the way the pizzas turned out. Teacher supervision for any cutting or use of the stove is mandatory.

Measurement in the Kitchen!

You will need:

1 cup flour
2 tsp baking powder
$\frac{1}{2}$ tsp salt

Mix together in a bowl.

4 tbsp olive oil
4 tbsp milk
2 eggs

Mix together and add to dry ingredients. Stir until dough is stiff.

Spaghetti or pizza sauce
Your favorite pizza toppings (pepperoni, green pepper, pineapple, mushrooms, olives, etc.)
Bowls
Wooden spoon
Rolling pin
Greased cookie sheet

Oven 375° F

Learning About Measurement **Name:** _____

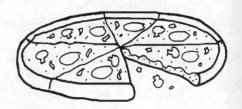

Method:

When the dough is stiff, sprinkle some flour onto a large piece of $\frac{1}{2}$ in.^{2} graph paper that is on a table top.

Sprinkle flour onto rolling pin.

Roll out the dough until it is .25 in. ($\frac{1}{4}$ in.) thick. It can be any shape that you like. (Square or rectangle will be easiest to measure.)

Estimate the area of the dough. _____

Fill a clean eye dropper with sauce. Mark around the dough with a trace of sauce.

Carefully remove the dough from the $\frac{1}{4}$ in.^{2} grid paper.

You should be able to see the outline of your pizza. Count the total number of squares that were covered by your pizza. _____

Prepare the Pizza!

Measure some sauce. Spoon on thin layer of the sauce.

Measure how much of each topping you are putting on your pizza.

We put on _____ tsp of sauce.

We put on _____ tsp of _____ .

We put on _____ tsp of _____ .

We put on _____ tsp of _____ .

We put on _____ tsp of _____ .

Your teacher will put the pizza in the oven. Set the timer for 18 minutes for smaller pizzas or 25 minutes for larger ones. (Check the oven after 15 minutes!)

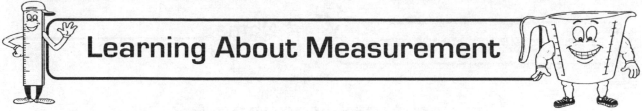

Learning About Measurement

Thinking About Measurement Activity Card 1

Choose an object from home and put it in a bag.

Show the bag to the class and give them any three hints about it. (i.e., It is a toy. It is smaller than my pillow. I sleep with it.)

Then, half the class will take turns asking you questions about it that only have to do with measurement. (i.e., Does it have a weight greater than a basketball? It is shorter than my arm? Could it fit into a quart carton?) The other half of the class will take turns asking you questions that do not have to do with measurement? (Is it made of wood? What color is it? Can it bend?)

After the item is guessed, discuss which half of the class got better information about the object. Were the questions about measurement more useful, less useful, equally useful or did the class need both kinds of questions to figure out the answer?

Learning About Measurement   **Name:** _____

Thinking About Measurement Card 2

You are at the post office.

1. Draw a postal worker at the counter.

2. Draw a box on the scale.

3. What is in the box? _____

4. Print the weight of the package on the scale.

Note to Teacher: This activity is a good summary of each of the four strands of measurement that was covered in this unit.

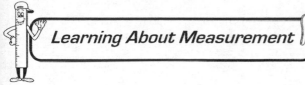

Name: _____

Thinking About Measurement Activity Card 3

Materials:

- a potato that has been cut in half

- scale and weights

- some paint in a dish

- a strip of paper

- a whole sheet of paper

- a small box (i.e., Kleenex box)

Estimate how many ounces your potato half weighs. _____

Make sure your potato is clean and dry. Find the weight of your potato and record the answer. _____

Estimate how many potato prints will fit across the strip of paper. _____

Neatly make the potato prints across the strip and record the answer.

_____

Estimate how many potato prints it will take to cover the sheet of paper.

_____

Neatly make the potato prints on the paper and record the answer.

_____

Estimate how many potato prints will fit on the outside of the box. _____

Neatly cover the box with potato prints and record the answer. _____

Learning About Measurement

Name: _____

Thinking About Measurement Activity Card 4

Materials:

- chalk
- measuring tape
- pencil
- paper

On a sunny day, take your students outside. Have them get into groups of two.

Repeat this activity three times during the day, in the morning, around noon, and later in the afternoon. Have one partner stand still while the other partner marks, with chalk, the beginning and the end of their shadow. Measure the length of the shadow. Repeat with the other partner.

Compare the length of the shadows at each time of the day.

	Morning	**Noon**	**Afternoon**
Partner #1			
Partner #2			

In the morning, _____ shadow _____ long.

At noon, _____ shadow _____ long.

In the afternoon, _____shadow _____ long.

_____ shadow was longer at _____.

Learning About Measurement

Name: _____

Thinking About Measurement Activity Card 5

The owner of the local sports store wants to hold a contest to celebrate the 5th anniversary of his sports store. The prizes will be a BMX racing bike for first place, a skateboard for second prize, and a baseball, bat and glove for third prize. To win one of the prizes, you need to guess how many jellybeans it will take to fill a jar that has been placed in the front of the store.

How would you estimate the number of jelly beans it will take?

Good luck!

Show your work here.

I estimate you will need _____ jelly beans to fill the jar.

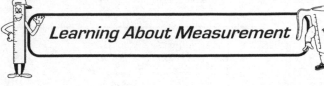

Word Search

Find as many words as you can that you use when talking about measurement.

```
x w r q a e b l m t e y y a r e k o c d
a l f t i r p i g r e a t i n g h e o b
v s t a c k p g e t b r i a o c e d v u
q f e v b a o h n i t d i s q u a r e s
v u n i t s i t h n n r i v q b v o r t
h i s o c t m b e c t l e y h i y o u r
w a p i o u n c e h o l d s i c k m w q
c a a c u b e v k e l o m i l e u m a l
l q c t n b e d a s o n v e t b i t s d
y a e s t i m a t e d g r o w l w a d y
i t s c a p a c i t y o u r w a l l e c
h o l d f e q b m e a s u r e u m l a o
a m e v e m t i a r e a n s i t b o o n
p i v u e p t b s e r e n a g r i d i t
p q e n t t h a s h o r t f h y r i a a
y u l r t y i u v a b s v t t f a r o i
d a a q r m u R m u r c o w h u n t i n
l r f r z x p o u r o f l i y l a c d d
d t t h l m t f s y m i l l i l i t e r
o t h h e i g h t i l l x a v i e r s o
b b r t o p e x a y r l f y a h u l y e
```

area	bits	inches	container	count	cover
cube	cubic	empty	estimate	far	fill
full	ounce	grid	heavy	height	hold
mile	length	level	light	quart	long
mass	measure	yard	feet	pour	short
space	squares	stack	tall	units	weight

 **Learning About Measurement**

Name: _____

My Measurement Journal

Date: _____

The activitity I did today was:

_____

_____

_____

I learned:

_____

_____

Next time I will:

_____

_____

Picture of today's activity.

Linear

Name: _____

Weight

Name: _____

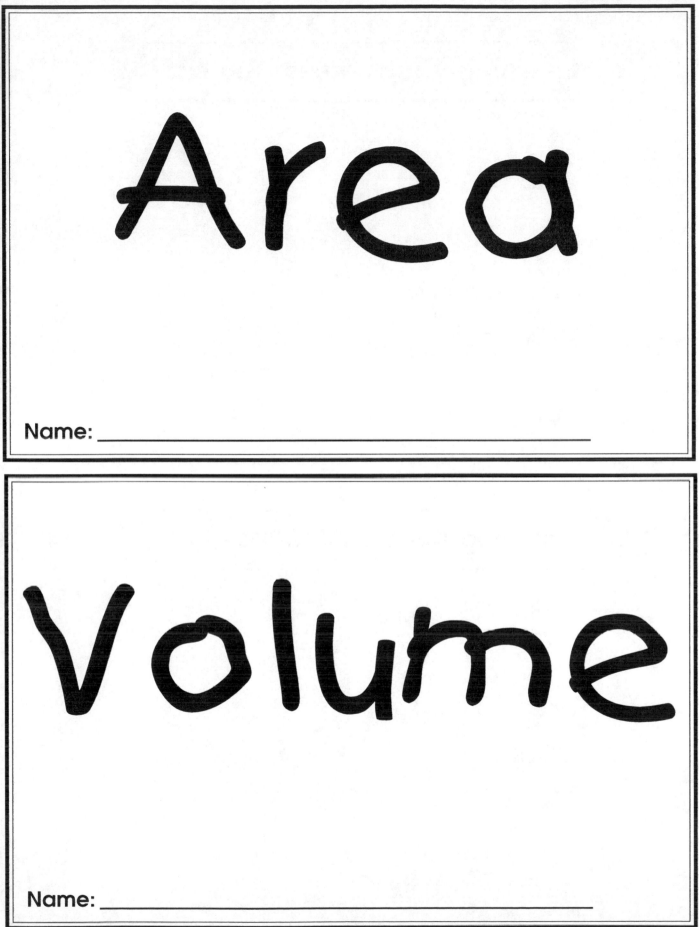

Area

Name: _____

Volume

Name: _____

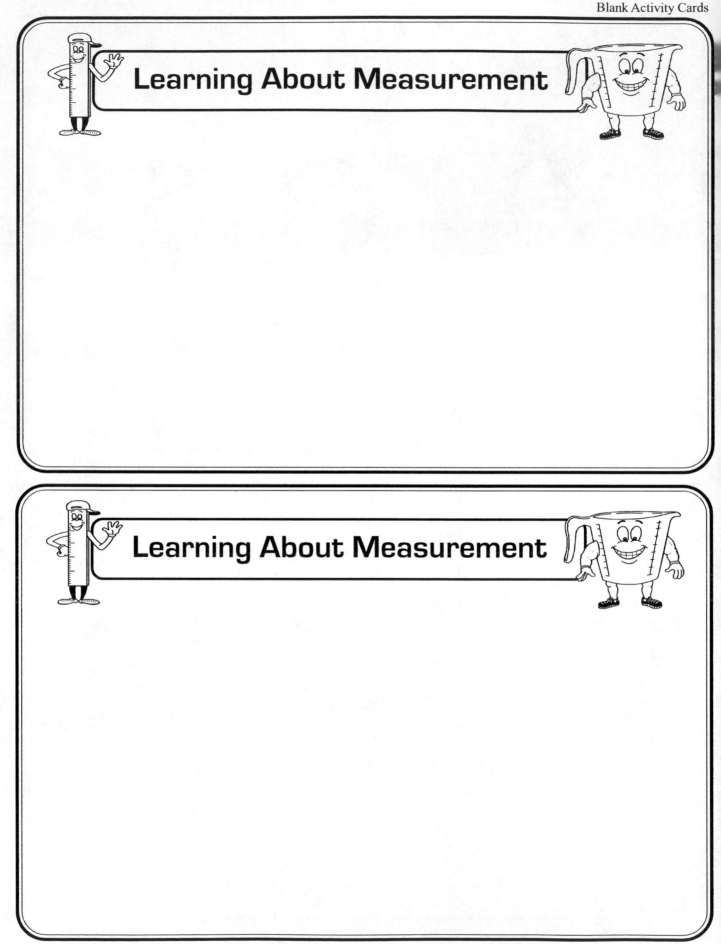

Learning About Measurement

Learning About Measurement

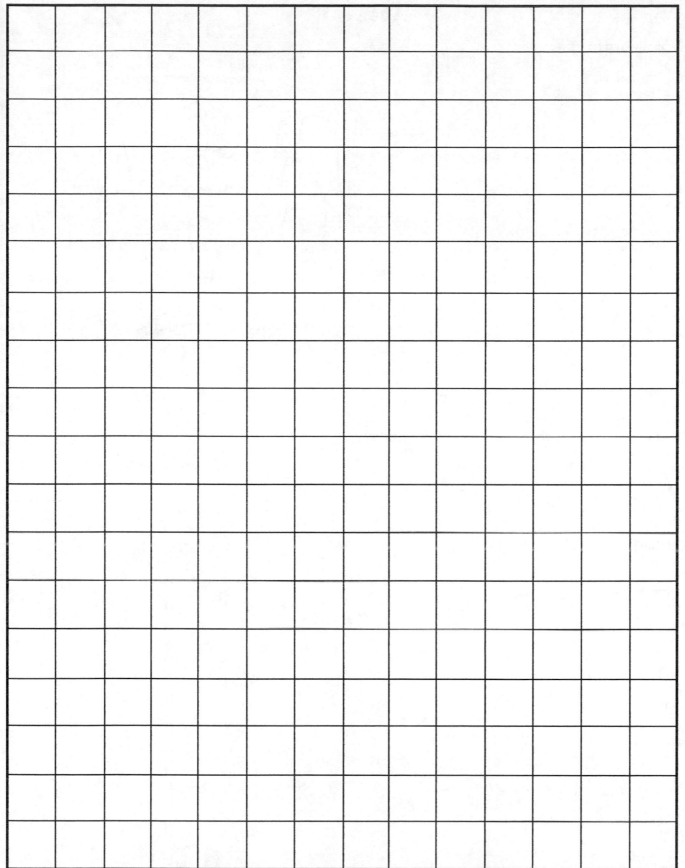

$\frac{1}{4}$ inch grid paper

Answer Key

Phonics Card 3: *(page 18)*
1. coffee
2. Christmas
3. crayon
4. candy
5. clown
6. carpet
7. calendar
8. coat
9. California
10. cube

Phonics Card 4: *(page 19)*
1. short **e**
2. long **u**
3. long **e**
4. short **a**
5. short **o**
6. long **i**
7. long **o**
8. short **e**
9. long **e**
10. long **a**

Word Study Card 2: *(page 21)*

1 Syllable	**2 Syllables**	**3 Syllables**	**4 Syllables**
length	ruler	area	capacity
width	measure		
inch	shorte		
miles	farthest		
foot			

Word Study Card 3: *(page 22)*
area
balance
container
count
cube
estimate
fill
length
mile
pound
pour
rulers
weigh

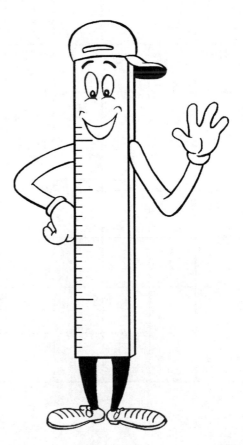

Word Study Card 4: *(page 23)*
1. near
2. full
3. big
4. short
5. wide
6. different
7. fat
8. hard
9. young
10. day

Word Study Card 5: *(page 24)*
Answers may vary.

Linear Activity Card 3: *(page 28)*
Pencil, baby and shoe are measured in in.

Linear Activity Card 10: *(page 35)*
  1. c)   **2.** a)   **3.** b)

Area Activity Card 3: *(page 38)*
Carpet, kitchen and curtains are measured in yd².

Area Activity Card 10: *(page 45)*
  1. b)   **2.** c)   **3.** a)   **4.** b)   **5.** a)

Weight Activity Card 3: *(page 48)*
Cereal, macaroni and packages are measured in ounces.

Weight Activity Card 8: *(page 53)*
The balloons filled with air will have a higher mass. Air does have mass.

Weight Activity Card 10: *(page 55)*
  1. b)   **2.** a)   **3.** c)   **4.** c)   **5.** b)

Volume and Capacity Card 3: *(page 58)*
medicine, rainfall and pop in a can are measured in ounces.

Volume and Capacity Activity Card 10: *(page 65)*
  1. c)   **2.** a)   **3.** c)   **4.** b)   **5.** a)

Matching Activity Card 1: *(page 66)*
  1. ruler   **2.** container   **3.** scale   **4.** area   **5.** mile

Reading Activity Card 1: *(page 73)*
  1. The King ordered a bed for the Queen.
  2. He measured the size of bed that would fit the Queen with his feet.
  3. He asked for a bed 6 feet by 3 feet.
  4. The bed was too small because the apprentice had smaller feet than the King.
  5. to have a standard unit of measure

Math Activity Card 1: *(page 75)*
  1. inch
  2. yard
  3. mile
  4. in.
  5. yd.
  6. mi.
  7. 36
  8. 1 760
  9. Answers may vary
 10. Answers may vary
 11. Answers may vary

Math Activity Card 2: *(page 76)*
  1. pint
  2. quart
  3. oz.
  4. qt.
  5. 32 oz.
  6. Answers may vary.
  7. Answers may vary.
  8. 64 oz.
  9. The amount that can be held in something.
 10. 10 cups

Math Activity Card 3: *(page 77)*

1. ounce
2. pound
3. oz.
4. lb.
5. 16
6. 36
7. Answers may vary.
8. Answers may vary.
9. a scale

Math Activity Card 4: (page 78)

1. Jenny walked 15 yards.
2. The throwers in order from the shortest to farthest are Ellen, Paula, Marc.
3. The trip to Grandma's house was 500 yds. + 800 yds. = 1 300 yds. The trip home was 1 mi. = 1 760 yds. Therefore, the trip to Grandma's was 1 760 yds. - 1 300 yds. = 460 yds. longer.
4. 46 in. - 36 in. = 10 in. Therefore, Constance is 10 in. taller than Joelle.
5. The presents in order from lightest to heaviest are Kelly's, Heather's, Dorothy's.

Math Activity Card 5: *(page 79)*

6. The items in order from the lightest to the heaviest: balloon, pencil, orange, soccer ball, computer.
7. 8 oz. + 16 oz. + 6 oz. = 30 oz. Joyce bought 30 oz. of mixed nuts.
8. 2 qts. + 1 qt. = 3 qts. Adam bought 3 qts. of drinks.
9. 10 oz. + 30 oz. = 40 oz.   1 qt. = 32 oz.   Therefore, Diego bought more yogurt.
10. The stuffed toys were the biggest. The videos were the smallest.

Math Activity Card 6: *(page 80)*

1. shorter
2. lighter
3. Lady
4. 24 in.
5. pounds

Word Search: *(page 88)*

Code #	Title and Grade

See Dealer or www.onthemarkpress.com For Pricing 1-800-463-6367

TM-1114 A Graph for all Seasons Gr. 1-3
TM-1492 Abel's Island LL Gr. 4-6
TM-2504 Addition Gr. 1-3
TM-1128 Addition Drills Gr. 1-3
TM-1131 Addition & Subtraction Drills Gr. 1-3
TM-14174 Adv. of Huckle Berry Finn LL Gr. 7-8
TM-293 All About Dinosaurs Gr. 2
TM-102 All About Mexico Gr. 4-6
TM-120 All About the Ocean Gr. 5-7
TM-249 All About the Sea Gr. 4-6
TM-261 All About Weather Gr. 7-8
OTM-2110 All Kinds of Structures Gr. 1
OTM-601 Amazing Aztecs Gr. 4-6
OTM-1468 Amelia Bedelia LL Gr. 1-3
OTM-113 America The Beautiful Gr. 4-6
OTM-1457 Amish Adventure LL Gr. 7-8
OTM-602 Ancient China Gr. 4-6
OTM-618 Ancient Egypt Gr. 4-6
OTM-621 Ancient Greece Gr. 4-6
OTM-619 Ancient Rome Gr. 4-6
OTM-1453 Anne of Green Gables LL Gr. 7-8
OTM-1622 Australia B/W Pictures
OTM-105 Australia Gr. 5-8
OTM-14224 Banner in the Sky LL Gr. 7-8
OTM-401 Be Safe Not Sorry Gr. P-1
OTM-1409 Bear Tales in Literature Gr. 2-4
OTM-14202 Bears in Literature Gr. 1-3
OTM-14257 Because of Winn-Dixie LL Gr. 4-6
OTM-1853 Beginning Manuscript Gr. PK-2
OTM-1854 Beginning Cursive Gr. 2-4
OTM-1857 Beginning and Practice Manuscript Gr. PK-2
OTM-1858 Beginning and Practice Cursive Gr. 2-4
OTM-14114 Best Christmas Pageant Ever LL Gr. 4-6
OTM-14107 Borrowers, The LL Gr. 4-6
OTM-1463 Bridge to Terabithia LL Gr. 4-6
OTM-2516 La Numeration/Numeration 1-3
OTM-2517 L'addition/Addition Gr. 1-3
OTM-2518 La Soustraction/Subtraction 1-3
OTM-2519 Les Sons/Phonics Gr. 1-3
OTM-2520 La Comprehension de Textes/ Reading for Meaning Gr. 1-3
OTM-2521 Les Majuscules et la Ponctuation/ Cap. and Punctuation. Gr. 1-3
OTM-2522 La Redaction de Phrases/ Sentence Writing Gr. 1-3
OTM-2523 La Redaction de Textes/ Story Writing Gr. 1-3
OTM-2524 BTS Numeración Gr. 1-3
OTM-2525 BTS Adición Gr. 1-3
OTM-2526 BTS Sustracción Gr. 1-3
OTM-2527 BTS Fonética Gr. 1-3
OTM-2528 BTS Leer para Entender Gr. 1-3
OTM-2529 BTS Uso de las Mayúsculas y Reglas de Puntuación Gr. 1-3
OTM-2530 BTS Composición de Oraciones Gr. 1-3
OTM-2531 BTS Composici13n de Historias Gr. 1-3
OTM-2513 BTS Handwriting Manuscript Gr. 1-3
OTM-2514 BTS Handwriting Cursive Gr. 1-3
OTM-2515 BTS Word Families Gr. 1-3
OTM-14256 Bud, Not Buddy LL Gr. 4-6
OTM-1805 Building Word Families #1 S.V. Gr. 1-2
OTM-1807 Building Word Families #2 L.V. Gr. 1-2
OTM-14164 Call It Courage LL Gr. 7-8
OTM-1467 Call of the Wild LL Gr. 7-8
OTM-2507 Capitalization & Punctuation Gr. 1-3
OTM-14198 Captain Courageous LL Gr. 7-8
OTM-14154 Castle in the Attic LL Gr. 4-6

OTM-631 Castles & Kings Reading Level 2-4 Gr. 4-6
OTM-1434 Cats in Literature Gr. 3-6
OTM-14212 Cay, The LL Gr. 7-8
OTM-2107 Cells, Tissues & Organs Gr. 7-8
OTM-2101 Characteristics of Flight Gr. 4-6
OTM-1466 Charlie and the Chocolate Factory LL Gr. 4-6
OTM-109 Charlotte's Web LL Gr. 4-6
OTM-1470 Chocolate Fever LL Gr. 4-6
OTM-14241 Chocolate Touch LL Gr. 4-6
OTM-14104 Classical Poetry Gr. 7-12
OTM-811 Community Helpers Gr. 1-3
OTM-14183 Copper Sunrise NS Gr. 7-8
OTM-1486 Corduroy and Pocket for Corduroy LL Gr. 1-3
OTM-234 Creatures of the Sea Gr. 2-4
OTM-14208 Curse of the Viking Grave LL Gr. 7-8
OTM-1121 Data Management Gr. 4-6
OTM-253 Dealing with Dinosaurs Gr. 4-6
OTM-14105 Dicken's Christmas LL Gr. 7-8
OTM-1621 Dinosaurs B/W Pictures
OTM-216 Dinosaurs Gr. 1
OTM-14175 Dinosaurs in Literature Gr. 1-3
OTM-2106 Diversity of Living Things Gr. 4-6
OTM-1127 Division Drills Gr. 4-6
OTM-287 Down by the Sea Gr. 1-3
OTM-14416 Dragons in Literature Gr. 3-6
OTM-2109 Earth's Crust Gr. 6-8
OTM-1612 Egypt B/W Pictures
OTM-14255 Egypt Game LL Gr. 4-6
OTM-628 Egyptians Today and Yesterday Gr. 2-3
OTM-2108 Electricity Gr. 4-6
OTM-285 Energy: The World & You Gr. 4-6
OTM-2123 Environment, The Gr. 4-6
OTM-1812 ESL Teaching Ideas Gr. K-8
OTM-14258 Esperanza Rising NS Gr. 4-6
OTM-1822 Exercises in Grammar Gr. 6
OTM-1823 Exercises in Grammar Gr. 7
OTM-1824 Exercises in Grammar Gr. 8
OTM-1054 Exploring Canada Gr. 1-3
OTM-1056 Exploring Canada Gr. 1-6
OTM-1055 Exploring Canada Gr. 4-6
OTM-820 Exploring My School and Community Gr. 1
OTM-1415 Fables Gr. 4-6
OTM-1639 Fables B/W Pictures
OTM-14210 Fantastic Mr. Fox LL Gr. 4-6
OTM-14168 First 100 Sight Words Gr. 1
OTM-14261 Flat Stanley LL Gr. 1-3
OTM-14170 Flowers for Algernon LL Gr. 7-8
OTM-14128 Fly Away Home LL Gr. 4-6
OTM-405 Food: Fact, Fun & Fiction Gr. 1-3
OTM-406 Food: Nutrition & Invention Gr. 4-6
OTM-2118 Force and Motion Gr. 1-3
OTM-2119 Force and Motion Gr. 4-6
OTM-14263 Fractured Fairy Tales LL Gr. 1-3
OTM-14172 Freckle Juice LL Gr. 1-3
OTM-14260 Frindle LL Gr. 4-6
OTM-1849 Fun with Phonics Gr. 1-3
OTM-14209 Giver, The LL Gr. 7-8
OTM-1490 Great Expectations LL Gr. 7-8
OTM-14169 Great Gilly Hopkins LL Gr. 4-6
OTM-14238 Greek Mythology Gr. 7-8
OTM-2113 Growth and Change in Animals Gr. 2-3
OTM-2114 Growth and Change in Plants Gr. 2-3
OTM-2104 Habitats Gr. 4-6
OTM-14205 Harper Moon LL Gr. 7-8
OTM-14136 Hatchet LL Gr. 7-8
OTM-14184 Hobbit LL Gr. 7-8
OTM-14250 Holes LL Gr. 4-6
OTM-14133 How To Eat Fried Worms LL 4-6
OTM-1848 How To Give a Presentation Gr. 4-6
OTM-14125 How To Teach Writing Through Gr. 7-9
OTM-1810 How To Write a Composition Gr. 6-10
OTM-1809 How To Write a Paragraph Gr. 5-10
OTM-1808 How To Write an Essay Gr. 7-12
OTM-1803 How To Write Poetry and Stories Gr. 4-6
OTM-407 Human Body Gr. 2-4
OTM-402 Human Body Gr. 4-6
OTM-605 In Days of Yore Gr. 4-6

OTM-606 In Pioneer Days Gr. 2-4
OTM-241 Incredible Dinosaurs Gr. P-1
OTM-14177 Incredible Journey LL Gr. 4-6
OTM-14100 Indian in the Cupboard LL Gr. 4-6
OTM-14193 Island of the Blue Dolphins LL 4-6
OTM-1465 James & The Giant Peach LL 4-6
OTM-1625 Japan B/W Pictures
OTM-106 Japan Gr. 5-8
OTM-14264 Journey to the Center of the Earth LL Gr. 7-8
OTM-1461 Julie of the Wolves NS Gr. 7-8
OTM-502 Junior Music for Fall Gr. 4-6
OTM-505 Junior Music for Spring Gr. 4-6
OTM-506 Junior Music Made Easy for Winter Gr. 4-6
OTM-1862 Just for Boys – Reading Composition Gr 3-6
OTM-1863 Just for Boys – Reading Composition Gr. 6-8
OTM-298 Learning About Dinosaurs Gr. 3
OTM-1122 Learning About Measurement Gr. 1-3
OTM-1119 Learning About Money Gr. 1-3
OTM-1123 Learning About Numbers Gr. 1-3
OTM-269 Learning About Rocks & Soils 2-3
OTM-1108 Learning About Shapes Gr. 1-3
OTM-2100 Learning About Simple Machines Gr. 1-3
OTM-1104 Learning About the Calendar Gr. 2-3
OTM-1110 Learning About Time Gr. 1-3
OTM-1450 Legends Gr. 4-6
OTM-14130 Life & Adv. of Santa Claus LL 7-8
OTM-210 Life in a Pond Gr. 3-4
OTM-630 Life in the Middle Ages Gr. 7-8
OTM-2103 Light & Sound Gr. 4-6
OTM-14219 Light in the Forest LL Gr. 7-8
OTM-1446 Lion, Witch and the Wardrobe LL Gr. 4-6
OTM-1851 Literature Response Forms Gr. 1-3
OTM-1852 Literature Response Forms Gr. 4-6
OTM-14233 Little House on the Prairie LL 4-6
OTM-14109 Lost in the Barrens LL Gr. 7-8
OTM-278 Magnets Gr. 3-5
OTM-403 Making Sense of Our Senses K-1
OTM-294 Mammals Gr. 1
OTM-295 Mammals Gr. 2
OTM-296 Mammals Gr. 3-4
OTM-297 Mammals Gr. 5-6
OTM-14160 Maniac Magee LL Gr. 4-6
OTM-119 Mapping Activities & Outlines! 4-8
OTM-117 Mapping Skills Gr. 1-3
OTM-107 Mapping Skills Gr. 4-6
OTM-2116 Matter & Materials Gr. 1-3
OTM-2117 Matter & Materials Gr. 4-6
OTM-1116 Measurement Gr. 4-8
OTM-1609 Medieval Life B/W Pictures
OTM-270 Microscopy Gr. 5-8
OTM-1413 Mice in Literature Gr. 3-5
OTM-14180 Midnight Fox LL Gr. 4-6
OTM-1118 Money Talks Gr. 3-6
OTM-1443 Monkeys in Literature Gr. 2-4
OTM-1497 Mouse & the Motorcycle LL Gr. 4-6
OTM-1494 Mr. Poppers Penguins LL Gr. 4-6
OTM-14201 Mrs. Frisby & Rats LL Gr. 4-6
OTM-1826 Multi-Level Spelling USA Gr. 3-6
OTM-1132 Multiplication & Division Drills 4-6
OTM-1130 Multiplication Drills Gr. 4-6
OTM-114 My Country! The USA! Gr. 2-4
OTM-1437 Mystery at Blackrock Island LL 7-8
OTM-14157 Nate the Great and Sticky Case LL Gr. 1-3
OTM-110 New Zealand Gr. 4-8
OTM-1475 Novel Ideas Gr. 4-6
OTM-14244 Number the Stars LL Gr. 4-6
OTM-2503 Numeration Gr. 1-3
OTM-1459 On the Banks of Plum Creek LL 4-6
OTM-14220 One In the Middle Is Green Kangaroo LL Gr. 1-3
OTM-272 Our Trash Gr. 2-3
OTM-2121 Our Universe Gr. 5-8
OTM-286 Outer Space Gr. 1-2
OTM-118 Outline Maps of the World Gr. 1-8
OTM-1431 Owls in the Family LL Gr. 4-6
OTM-1452 Paperbag Princess LL Gr. 1-3
OTM-212 Passport to Australia Gr. 4-5
OTM-1804 Personal Spelling Dictionary Gr. 2-5
OTM-503 Phantom of the Opera Gr. 6-9
OTM-2506 Phonics Gr. 1-3
OTM-1133 Picture Book Math Gr. 1-3
OTM-1448 Pigs in Literature Gr. 2-4
OTM-1499 Pinballs LL Gr. 4-6

OTM-634 Pirates Gr. 4-6
OTM-2120 Planets Gr. 3-6
OTM-1874 Poetry Prompts Gr. 1-3
OTM-1875 Poetry Prompts Gr. 4-6
OTM-624 Prehistoric Times Gr. 4-6
OTM-1855 Practice Manuscript Gr. PK-2
OTM-1856 Practice Cursive Gr. 2-4
OTM-501 Primary Music for Fall Gr. 1-3
OTM-504 Primary Music for Spring Gr. 4-6
OTM-507 Primary Music for Winter Gr. 1-3
OTM-14262 Prince Caspian LL Gr. 4-6
OTM-1120 Probability and Inheritance Gr. 7-10
OTM-1426 Rabbits in Literature Gr. 2-4
OTM-1444 Ramona Quimby Age 8 LL 4-6
OTM-2508 Reading for Meaning Gr. 1-3
OTM-1876 Reading Logs Gr. K-1
OTM-1877 Reading Logs Gr. 2-3
OTM-14162 Reading with Arnold Lobel Gr. 2-3
OTM-14234 Reading with Arthur Gr. 1-3
OTM-1440 Reading with Beatrix Potter 2-4
OTM-14129 Reading with Beatrix Potter: Biography Gr. 2-4
OTM-14200 Reading with Curious George Gr. 2-4
OTM-14230 Reading with Eric Carle Gr. 1-3
OTM-14126 Reading with Franklin Gr. 1-3
OTM-14251 Reading with Kenneth Oppel 4-6
OTM-1427 Reading with Mercer Mayer 1-2
OTM-14171 Reading with Phoebe Gilman Gr. 2-3
OTM-14142 Reading with Robert Munsch Gr. 1-3
OTM-14140 Reading with Kids at Bailey Elem. School Gr. 2-4
OTM-14167 Reading with Magic School Bus Gr. 1-3
OTM-14247 Reading with Magic Treehouse Gr. 1-3
OTM-14225 River, The LL Gr. 7-8
OTM-508 Robert Schumann-Life & Times Gr. 6-9
OTM-265 Rocks & Minerals Gr. 4-6
OTM-14103 Sadako and 1 000 Paper Cranes LL Gr. 4-6
OTM-404 Safety Gr. 2-4
OTM-1442 Sarah Plain & Tall LL Gr. 4-6
OTM-1601 Sea Creatures B/W Pictures
OTM-279 Sea Creatures Gr. 1-3
OTM-1464 Secret Garden LL Gr. 4-6
OTM-2502 Sentence Writing Gr. 1-3
OTM-1430 Serendipity Series Gr. 3-5
OTM-1866 Shakespeare Shorts – Performing Arts Gr. 2-4
OTM-1867 Shakespeare Shorts – Performing Arts Gr. 4-6
OTM-1868 Shakespeare Shorts – Language Arts Gr. 2-4
OTM-1869 Shakespeare Shorts – Language Arts Gr. 4-6
OTM-14158 Shilo LL Gr. 4 6
OTM-14181 Sight Word Activities Gr. 1
OTM-299 Simple Machines Gr. 4-6
OTM-2122 Solar System Gr. 4-6
OTM-111 South American Countries Gr. 4-6
OTM-1644 South American B/W Pictures
OTM-205 Space Gr. 2-3
OTM-1814 Spelling Gr. 1
OTM-1815 Spelling Gr. 2
OTM-1816 Spelling Gr. 3
OTM-1817 Spelling Gr. 4
OTM-1818 Spelling Gr. 5
OTM-1819 Spelling Gr. 6
OTM-1834 Spelling Blacklines Gr. 1
OTM-1835 Spelling Blacklines Gr. 2
OTM-1836 Spelling Blacklines Gr. 3
OTM-1837 Spelling Blacklines Gr. 4
OTM-1827 Spelling Worksavers #1 Gr. 3-5
OTM-2125 Stable Structures & Mech. Gr. 3
OTM-14139 Stone Fox LL Gr. 4-6
OTM-14214 Stone Orchard LL Gr. 7-8
OTM-1864 Story Starters Gr. 1-3
OTM-1865 Story Starters Gr. 4-6
OTM-1873 Story Starters Gr. 1-6
OTM-2509 Story Writing Gr. 1-3
OTM-2111 Structures, Mechanisms & Motion Gr. 2
OTM-14211 Stuart Little LL Gr. 4-6
OTM-2505 Subtraction Gr. 1-3
OTM-1129 Subtraction Drills Gr. 1-3

Code #	Title and Grade
OTM-2511	Successful Language Practice Gr. 1-3
OTM-2512	Successful Math Practice Gr. 1-3
OTM-2309	Summer Learning Gr. K-1
OTM-2310	Summer Learning Gr. 1-2
OTM-2311	Summer Learning Gr. 2-3
OTM-2312	Summer Learning Gr. 3-4
OTM-2313	Summer Learning Gr. 4-5
OTM-2314	Summer Learning Gr. 5-6
OTM-14159	Summer of the Swans LL Gr. 4-6
OTM-1418	Superfudge LL Gr. 4-6
OTM-108	Switzerland Gr. 4-6
OTM-115	Take a Trip to Australia Gr. 2-3
OTM-2102	Taking Off With Flight Gr. 1-3
OTM-1455	Tales of the Fourth Grade LL 4-6
OTM-1135	Teaching Math Through Sports Gr. 5-8
OTM-1134	Teaching Math with Everyday Manipulatives Gr. 4-6
OTM-14259	The Tale of Despereaux LL Gr. 4-6
OTM-1472	Ticket to Curlew LL Gr. 4-6
OTM-14222	To Kill a Mockingbird LL Gr. 7-8
OTM-14163	Traditional Poetry Gr. 7-10
OTM-1481	Tuck Everlasting LL Gr. 4-6
OTM-14126	Turtles in Literature Gr. 1-3
OTM-1427	Unicorns in Literature Gr. 3-5
OTM-617	Viking Age, The Gr. 4-6
OTM-14206	War with Grandpa LL Gr. 4-6
OTM-2124	Water Gr. 2-4
OTM-260	Weather Gr. 4-6
OTM-1417	Wee Folk in Literature Gr. 3-5
OTM-808	What is a Community? Gr. 2-4
OTM-262	What is the Weather Today? 2-4
OTM-1473	Where the Red Fern Grows LL Gr. 7-8
OTM-1487	Where the Wild Things Are LL Gr. 1-3
OTM-14187	Whipping Boy LL Gr. 4-6
OTM-14226	Who is Frances Rain? LL Gr. 4-6
OTM-509	Wolfgang Amadeus Mozart Gr. 6-9
OTM-14213	Wolf Island LL Gr. 1-3
OTM-1859	Word Families 2, 3 Letter Words Gr. 1-3
OTM-1860	Word Families 3, 4 Letter Words Gr. 1-3
OTM-1861	Word Families 2, 3, 4 Letter Words Big Book Gr. 1-3
OTM-620	World Explorers Gr. 4-6
OTM-14221	Wrinkle in Time LL Gr. 7-8